The Dolls of Shelburne Museum

by Jean M. Burks

Fig. 162

Cover: Parian Lady, fig. 161; Papier-mâché Lady, fig. 52; Wax Girl, fig. 79; China Gentleman, fig. 110

ISBN: 0-939384-28-0

Photographs by J. David Bohl
Photograph by Sanders H. Milens on page 30

Graphic Design
Vicky McCafferty

Printed By
Transcontinental Printing, Montreal, Canada

Published By
Shelburne Museum, U.S. Route 7, P.O. Box 10, Shelburne Road, Shelburne, Vermont 05482

Table of Contents

Acknowledgements 1

Introduction 2

Key to Identification Labels 5

Technical Tidbits 6

Wooden Dolls 12

Papier-Mâché Dolls 36

Wax Dolls 56

China Dolls 70

Bisque Dolls 88

Parian-Type Dolls 106

Cloth Dolls 124

Notes 134

Appendices 137

Bibliography 140

Acknowledgements

The preparation of this catalogue, developed over five years,
would not have been possible without the talented assistance
of many individuals.

Darlene Gengelbach, doll historian, conservator, and former
colleague at the Strong Museum in Rochester, New York, served as
consultant to this project and meticulously examined and evaluated
each doll at the Shelburne Museum. Shelburne Museum conservators
Nancie Ravenel and Intern Jennifer Nicoll carefully prepared and
conserved our dolls for photography and exhibition. The collections
management staff—Cathi Comar, director, Barbara Rathburn, associate
registrar, Russ Symons and Zachary Ward, art handlers—each lent
their individual expertise to organize and track the movement of the
dolls during their many travels between exhibit, storage, conservation,
and photography over an extended period of time.

United Federation of Doll Clubs experts Jean Grout and
Diane Buck kindly and carefully reviewed and gave invaluable
comments on the content of the china and papier-mâché chapters
respectively. Margaret Spicer of the theater department at
Dartmouth College provided expertise on the history of undergarments. My sincere gratitude goes to Mary Krombholz, who
generously shared her groundbreaking knowledge and unpublished
research with me on German porcelain dolls. As a result of
numerous e-mails and telephone conversations we were able to
attribute all of the china and parian dolls in this catalogue to a
specific factory. I also extend my appreciation to Shelburne Museum
chief curator Henry Joyce, who meticulously read the completed
manuscript and offered invaluable editorial suggestions.

Very special thanks to photographer extraordinaire David Bohl,
who, with the talented assistance of Julie Yankowsky, Shelburne
Museum rights and reproduction manager, patiently posed our
distinguished ladies and gentlemen and captured these spectacular
images on film, which I hope all who read this catalog will enjoy.

Fig. 124

Introduction

I feel that I started collecting at about 10 years old. I had a wonderful grand-mother and she loved to make dolls for us children and I asked her when my birthday came and Christmas came, I said, 'Granny won't you please make me another doll'. . . Well, I loved those dolls. I looked at those dolls, but I never played with those dolls. And now as I've gotten into the field of the Museum, I went back into my attic I found those dolls; I'd kept them all those years. . . . When I was a young girl, my grandmother Matilda Adelaide Waldron Elder dressed small dolls as gifts for such special occasions as Christmas or my birthday. Instead of playing with them, I treasured them so much that I kept them together as a collection to enjoy. Hence they became my very first collection.[1]

The desire to possess many different examples of her favorite playthings led the adult Electra Havemeyer Webb eventually to accumulate more than five hundred dolls. They form part of an extraordinary fine, folk, and decorative arts collection of more than 150,000 artifacts housed in 35 historic structures that have been relocated from various places in the Northeast to the 33-acre campus of the Shelburne Museum near Vermont's Lake Champlain. The Shelburne Museum was founded in 1947 by Mrs. Webb (1888-1960), the daughter of sugar magnate H. O. Havemeyer and his wife Louisine, both distinguished collectors of Impressionist paintings. Electra inherited her parents' artistic enthusiasm, but her aesthetic interests were quite different, focused instead on acquiring the "everyday objects" in which she found beauty.

Fig. 1
Electra Havemeyer Webb
In second-floor east room
Variety Unit
1951 Scrapbook, EHW pa
Shelburne Museum Arch

Fig. 2
Bisque Dolls
Waltershausen, Thuringia, Germany
Kämmer & Reinhardt
About 1900
Tinted unglazed socket heads, blonde mohair wigs, glass sleep eyes,
open mouth with teeth, five-piece jointed composition bodies
Clothing made by Matilda Adelaide Waldron Elder
7"
20-1-29a-e
Gift of Electra Havemeyer Webb, 1954.374.1-5

Fig. 3
Bisque Dolls
Waltershausen, Thuringia, Germany
Kämmer & Reinhardt
About 1900
Tinted unglazed socket heads, blonde mohair wigs, glass sleep eyes,
open mouth with teeth, five-piece jointed composition bodies
Clothing made by Matilda Adelaide Waldron Elder
7"
20-1-29g, 20-1-29h
Gift of Mrs. Sheldon Tilney, 1959.78
Gift of Mr. George Frelinghuysen, 1963-125.36

Mrs. Webb had been acquiring for forty years before she purchased the first museum building to house her artifacts. In August 1946 she bought the old Weed property in Shelburne, Vermont, built in 1835 and later renamed the Variety Unit—a title that encapsulated the eclectic collections it came to exhibit. In 1948 she stated in a memo, "the largest collection I wish to install [here] in an attractive manner is my dolls and dollhouses."[2]

Shelburne Museum is also the repository of part of the important Chandler doll collection. After the death of Mabel Chandler (1874-1961), her daughters Mrs. Frederick Lee Moore and Mrs. Lawrence U. Jeffries (Mrs. F. C.) donated 150 dolls to the Shelburne Museum in 1962. Mrs. Chandler personally collected this distinguished grouping of European and American dolls dating from the early eighteenth through twentieth centuries, and her children divided her collection between the Shelburne Museum and the Worthington Historical Society in Columbus, Ohio.

Another key participant in the creation of Shelburne's doll collection was Marta Mengis, a Latvian refugee working as a seamstress in nearby Burlington who was employed at the Museum in 1953 after her son, Einars, became the museum's photographer. In 1962 museum director Sterling Emerson sent her to Ohio to choose which of Mrs. Chandler's dolls would become part of the collection. With this addition, Alice Marvin was hired as a researcher to create a catalog on the entire collection which, unfortunately, was never published due to lack of funds.

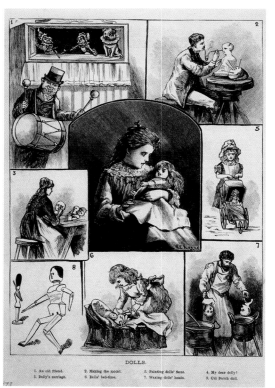

Dictionaries throughout the ages have defined "doll" in various ways. The English, French, and German words (poppet, *poupé,* and *puppe*) are derived from the Latin word, *pupa,* meaning a small figure that is a likeness of the human form. In terms of usage, a doll can be a child's plaything, but at times it has also been a religious image, fashion mannequin, educational tool, objet d'art, or an investment.[3] With this definition in mind, in this book I have omitted ceremonial religious figures (créche dolls), decorative half-figures (pincushions, pen-wipers, wedding cake figures), puppets, mechanical toys (automata), and dolls made of natural materials (shells, apples, nuts, ivory, bone, and rawhide).

The 350 dolls included in this catalog represent the finest and rarest examples from the Shelburne Museum's collection of 850. Traditionally they have been catalogued by the material used to fabricate the doll's head and include wood, papier mâché, wax, china, parian, bisque, cloth, rubber, and metal. The dolls date from about 1760 to 1930 and encompass European, Far Eastern, and American examples, both handmade and mass-produced. Dolls truly reflect the age in which they were made. They reveal the period's perceived ideal of beauty in their heads and faces, the perfect shape of the body for the fashions of the age, as well as the fashions themselves, and they ultimately serve as highly instructive instruments of social history.

Adult men and women, children *(bébés),* and toddlers as well as newborn infants are all represented. However, from the founding of the American colonies through the middle of the nineteenth century the elegant lady doll dominated the market. Such a plaything was meant to introduce a young girl to the feminine world of fashion, in dressing as well as dressmaking, and provided her the opportunity to earn skills that would be necessary later in life when, as Henri Rousseau observes, "in due time she will be her own doll" and live the life she once played. Society's attention continued to focus upon the potential adult within the child, grooming girls to become women.[4] Only after about 1850 did European factories begin producing porcelain child dolls in search of a "little mother" as recreation, leisure, and amusement for its own sake began to be considered natural among middle-class children. The emphasis was on contented domesticity, and baby dolls were very much the fashion in the nursery as were cradles, furniture, and doll china. By the end of the nineteenth century, the birthrate in this country had dropped, yet infant mortality remained unchanged, and it became the duty of the white middle-class woman to reproduce and safeguard the health of her children. Now knowledge of disease prevention was growing among the educated public, and a mother was obliged to become familiar with the new principles of sanitation, nutrition, and good health and to apply them assiduously to the care of her offspring.[5] This new awareness of child education and development impelled several creative, enterprising women to invent infant dolls with cuddly, washable, naturalistic bodies.

The publication of this catalog furthers the pioneering collecting, conservation and cataloging work initiated by Electra Havemeyer Webb, Mrs. George Chandler, Marta Mengis, and Alice Marvin. This catalog also publishes the results of innovative x-ray techniques to identify internal joints and mechanisms, incorporates new photography, and, after a two-year reinstallation and reinterpretation program, celebrates the reopening of the Shelburne Museum's distinguished doll collection in the Variety Unit in July 2004.

Key to Identification Labels

Doll Name Lady, gentleman, child (bébé), infant, based on molding of head and hair.

Place of Manufacture City and country, and state or district, if known.

Maker If known, the official name of the porcelain factory or doll maker as cited by the following sources:
Jürgen and Marianne Cieslik, *German Doll Encyclopedia*
Dorothy S. Coleman, Elizabeth Ann Coleman, and Evelyn Jane Coleman, *The Collector's Encyclopedia of Dolls*
Mary Krombholz, *Identifying German Chinas, 1840s-1930s*
The founding dates of these firms are listed in Appendix A.

Date Expressed as a date range ("about") which includes ten years both before and after that year.

Marks Letters, words, and numbers and how created (incised, painted, stamped, etc.) and where located on doll. Wherever possible, clothing was lifted to examine the head and body completely to locate marks.

Description Manufacturing materials and methods from top to bottom of doll. Some types of dolls require more detailed description than others. For example, the molded hairstyles on china and parian dolls are definitive characteristics that require greater delineation than do the hairstyles of the majority of wooden and papier-mâché dolls. However, if the details of the hairstyle are discussed in the accompanying caption, this information is omitted from the description in the identification label. Terminology is based on United Federation of Doll Club's (UFDC) glossary and Dorothy S. Coleman, Elizabeth Ann Coleman, and Evelyn Jane Coleman, *The Collector's Encyclopedia of Dolls*.

Costumes thought to be original to the doll have been listed as such in the caption; dolls known to have been redressed, according to written museum records, have also been described with the date and name of the person involved; clothing deemed to be inappropriate to the period of the doll has been removed and the body shown undressed. A large number of dolls in the catalogue have costumes that are stylistically correct but whose origin or age is unknown. If known, the costume material is included in the description.

Height Expressed in inches

Catalog Number Based on Shelburne Museum unique classification system as follows:
20-11-100, for example, means; doll (category 20) with a wooden head (category 11) given an arbitrary number (100) in that category.

Acquisition data Name of source and accession number as follows:
Webb Collection 1952-60 means dolls that Electra Havemeyer Webb acquired and installed in the Variety Unit building at Shelburne Museum for exhibition between the years 1952 and 1960.

Chandler Collection 1961-262-150 signifies the one hundred and fiftieth doll that the descendants of Mrs. George Brinton Chandler, the two-hundred-and-sixty-second donor to Shelburne Museum in 1961, gave the Shelburne Museum that year.

Gift of includes the name of donor, the year of the gift, the number of the donation that year to the Shelburne Museum and the arbitrary number of the item in that donor's gift.

Technical Tidbits

Nancie Ravenel

In preparation for this catalog, the opportunity to do some cursory technical research on the doll collection presented itself. As the collection was examined doll by doll, questions arose: What did internal mechanisms and joints look like? Can approximate dates or makers be ascribed to dolls based on technical examination? Although there are 850 dolls in the collection, conservators at the museum were not able to study a sufficient number from a technical point of view to draw any broad conclusions. However, some of their techniques and observations might be of use to doll historians in their own studies.

Collection History and Documentation

Dolls that come to the conservation lab for repair are given an extensive visual examination. Conservators describe in writing how the doll is made, note evidence of past repairs, and take photographs. They also research the files at the museum to determine if the doll has been repaired or redressed at the museum.

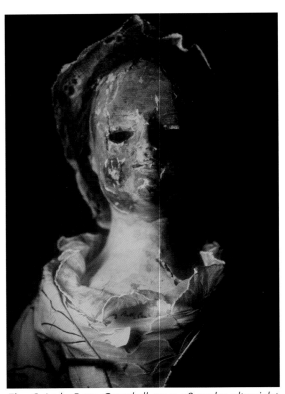

Fig. 6 *Lady Betty Campbell 20-11-98 under ultraviolet light, before conservation treatment. Overpaint appears very dark and white glue used to prevent the paint from flaking appears grey in color. The original varnish is yellow.*

In the early days of the Shelburne Museum (1947-56), researching and caring for the textiles and doll collections fell to Marthe Gianonni, formerly the governess to Mrs. Webb's children. Affectionately known as Mademoiselle (or Mlle.) she took her cues from Mary Whichelow, a dealer of antique dolls in Boston. As Mlle.'s health failed, Marta Mengis, who was working at the museum as a seamstress and guide, took responsibility for these collections.

In 1962, museum director Sterling Emerson sent Marta Mengis to select dolls from the Ohio collection of Mrs. George Chandler, which had been offered to the museum, to come to Shelburne. Mrs. Lawrence U. Jeffries, one of Mrs. Chandler's daughters, had compiled a list of dolls, noting those that had been redressed and who made the garments. This list is important because it also indicates which dolls were thought to be in their original garments at the time of the gift.

When this addition of 150 dolls came to Shelburne, researcher Alice Marvin was hired to write a catalog of the entire collection. Extensive work was undertaken on the doll collection at that time in preparation for the catalog which was ultimately never produced. Marta Mengis' son, Einars, photographed each doll in the collection in dressed and undressed states. Marta Mengis made notes on each doll's condition. Einars Mengis photographed dolls his mother had redressed in the older garments and newer garments. All of these documents provide each doll's treatment history and provenance for the dolls' garments.

Analytical Techniques

In present-day examinations, museum conservators use long- and short-wave ultraviolet lights to examine painted and varnished surfaces. Repainted areas do not fluoresce, appearing dark purple, under ultraviolet light. Many varnishes, glues, oils, and other materials fluoresce characteristically. Varnishes applied at different times fluoresce slightly differently from each other. While appearance under ultraviolet light is not enough to positively identify a material used, it can help determine if changes have been made to varnished and painted surfaces[1] (fig. 6).

A binocular microscope is helpful in looking closely at surfaces, particularly to examine painted surfaces on wooden dolls (fig. 7). In Shelburne's conservation lab, small paint samples from artifacts, about the size of a pinhead, can be mounted and examined in cross section using visible and ultraviolet microscopy techniques which allow conservators to characterize paint, ground, and varnish materials used. Polarized light microscopy can be used to identify pigments using a small dispersed paint. For the Queen Anne-style dolls, small samples containing the ground layer, paint layer, and varnish were mounted as cross sections and examined using Scanning Electron Microscopy with Energy Dispersive X-ray Spectroscopy (SEM/EDS) or Fourier-Transform Infrared spectroscopy (FTIR).[2] SEM/EDS provides information on elements present in pigment particles. FTIR indicates the organic materials present.

Fig. 7 *Detail of the eye painted on 20-11-107, before conservation treatment, magnified 100x with the Wild binocular microscope.*

For several wax and wax-over-papier-mâché-headed dolls, samples of wax coatings, about the size of a pinhead, were subjected to melting-point determination.[3] Melting points of waxes are characteristic of different kinds of waxes. Not only did the conservators learn at what temperature the dolls' heads soften, but they also could determine which were likely to be paraffin, having a melting point range of 52° to 57° C, and which were likely to be beeswax, with a melting point of 64° C.[4] Because beeswax fluoresces differently than paraffin or spermaceti waxes, conservators also examined the dolls under ultraviolet light and their surfaces were compared to known wax samples to characterize the material on the dolls.

To examine dolls' joints and mechanisms, conservators employed x-radiography[5] (fig. 8). X-ray opaque materials such as metals, lead, glass, and plaster appear whiter on the radiograph than materials that are more x-ray transparent, including fabric and wood. By reducing the amount of radiation that passes through the doll to the film, it is possible to image wood grain, papier mâché, and the materials used to stuff leather- and cloth-bodied dolls. Computer Aided Tomography (CT or CAT) is a radiographic technique that creates cross-sectional images. CT can provide valuable information about internal structure when an x-ray opaque material such as paint containing lead white obscures the image in a conventional radiograph (figs. 9 and 10).

Fig. 8 *Radiograph of wax over wood doll 20-10-24. The lace on the doll's collar and sleeves is made of metal thread.*

Conservators pursued analytical techniques in response to specific questions raised in the initial visual examinations and in order to help complete the information about the doll and its garments.

Fig. 9 *Queen Anne type doll 20-11-106 is ready for a CT.*

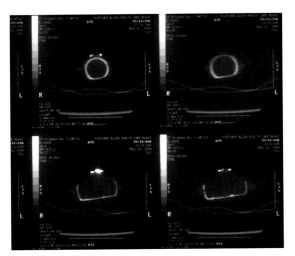

Fig. 10 *Some of the CT images generated of the head and chest of 20-11-106. The x-ray opaque material, probably a lead based paint, seen in the lower two images completely obscured the doll's chest in the conventional radiograph. Note the doll's glass eyes in the upper left image.*

A Real Lady Never Tells Her Age (Readily)

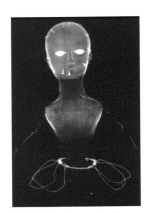

Fig. 11 *Radiograph of Queen Anne-type doll 20-11-87*

Fig. 13 *Radiograph of 20-11-118*

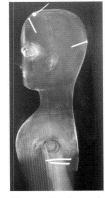

Fig. 14. *Radiograph detail, lateral view, of 20-11-118*

Fig. 12 *Radiograph detai[l] lateral view, of Queen Anne-type doll 20-11-87*

The twelve Queen Anne-type dolls in Shelburne's collection are the earliest, chronologically, and are highly prized. In an attempt to learn more about the specifics of their construction without removing delicate garments, each of the twelve dolls was radiographed. For ten dolls, the images indicated that the head, torso, and hips were lathe-turned and carved of a single hardwood block. Glass eyes were tear-drop shaped and wedged into the wooden head. Legs were attached by pegged mortise-and-tenon joints. Arms were attached in several ways: lower arms could be attached to textile or wire and then either nailed to the torso or passed through a hole bored through the torso from shoulder to shoulder (figs. 11 and 12).

The radiographs of the head and torso of the blond-haired Queen Anne-style doll (figs. 13 and 14) were greatly different from the other eleven dolls in the collection. The lateral radiograph showed that the doll's head and body were made from several pieces of wood. By comparing the lateral and flat views of the torso, one can see that the head and neck are made of three pieces of a hardwood. Joints are located through the center of the head from ear to ear and from the hairline of the forehead in an angle to just below the nose. From the lateral view radiography, one can see that the body was turned of softwood. The two pieces are held together with a mortise within the chest which is more evident on the flat view than the lateral view.

The arms are held with pinned mortise and tenons to dowels secured with[in] in the chest. Most startling, though, were remnants of an earlier set [of] globe-shaped blown glass eyes behind the tear-drop shaped glass ey[es] evident on the doll. Because blown glass eyes are associated with dolls [of] the second half of the nineteenth-century, the authenticity of this doll, pr[e]viously estimated to have been made about 1720 or 1730, was suspe[ct]. After reviewing this doll's radiograph, Bethnal Green Museum curator eme[r]itus Caroline Goodfellow suggested that the doll was a retooled artist[s] mannequin that might have been produced as late at the early twentie[th] century.[6]

One of the English wooden dolls could be dated, in part, based on the pigments found in the paint layers. In her study examining paint samples from these dolls using SEM/EDS, Betsy Geiser found that the ground layer on most of the Queen Anne-type dolls contained calcium carbonate (also known as chalk) and that the paint layer was composed of lead carbonate (or lead white) and calcium carbonate.[7] Since the lead white is x-ray opaque, the extent to which a doll's body is painted can also be determined with an x-ray without removing garments from the doll.

In the small English wood doll with the green silk bonnet (20-11-113), Geiser found that the ground contained calcium sulfate (gypsum) as well as calcium carbonate and that the paint layer contained barium sulfate as well as calcium carbonate. Barium sulfate was introduced as a pigment in 1782 and was available commercially from 1810 to 1820.[8] This doll, therefore, was not produced before 1810. This pigment difference would not be apparent in the radiograph because barium sulfate is as x-ray dense as lead white.

The Eyes Have It

Some eye mechanisms were mystifying. What does a flirt-eye mechanism look like? Is there any difference between a sleep-eye mechanisms in porcelain and wax heads?

Looking at a variety of heads and mechanism types necessarily meant that radiological techniques beyond the conventional might be called for to see what was going on inside the heads. Fluoroscopy used medically in functional studies of joints, and angiographic techniques are used to image the blood vessels around the heart. Both of these techniques produce moving radiographs, perfect for comparing functioning and nonfunctioning eye mechanisms. The images produced are positives in contrast to conventional negative radiographs. Therefore, materials that are more x-ray opaque appear darker. Because angiographic techniques

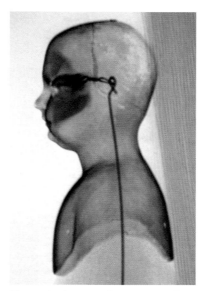

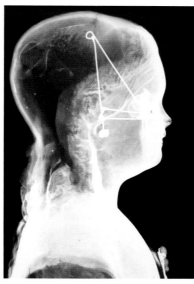

Fig. 15 *Angiogram of wax-over-papier mâché-headed doll 20-10-9*

Fig. 16 *Radiograph of flirt-eyed papier-mâché-headed doll 20-5-41*

are designed to look at soft tissue, they were applied to a number of poured wax- and wax-over-papier-mâché-headed dolls. Fluoroscopy was used on ceramic heads.

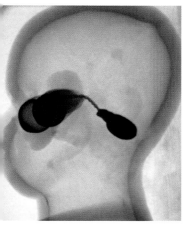

For the wired-eye mechanism in a wax-over-papier-mâché doll, spherical glass eyes are affixed to each end of a wire twisted over on itself at its center (fig. 15). The twists at the center of this wire form a loop through which a second wire is looped. This second wire continues downward through the body, emerging at the hip to form a pull.

The radiograph (fig. 16) of a flirt-eye mechanism in a German papier-mâché-headed doll made about 1860 shows a pendulum with a lead weight. The eyes are secured to the

Fig. 17 *Angiogram of wax headed doll 20-10-41*

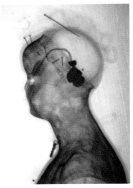

Fig. 18 *Angiogram of wax-over-papier-mâché doll 20-10-53*

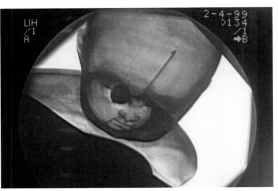

Fig. 19 *Fluroscopic image of wax-over-papier-mâché taufling 20-10-14*

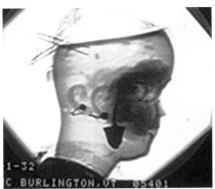

Fig. 20 *Fluoroscopic image of Simon and Halbig doll 20-1-32*

reverse side of the face by means of a putty. Sleep eyes are also set to the reverse side of the doll's face with a putty material. The eyes are connected to each other and to a lead weight with wire. Though the mechanisms are the same, the shape of the weight and method of attaching the weight to the eyes vary. Images from an English poured wax head of about 1875 attributed to John Edwards (fig. 17), a German wax-over-papier-mâché-headed doll made about 1870 (fig. 18), a wax-over-

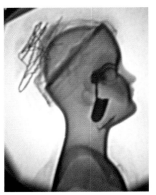

Fig. 21 *Fluroscopic image of Kestner Co. doll 20-1-41*

papier-mâché-headed taufling of about 1880 (fig. 19), a doll with a head made by Simon and Halbig of about 1910 (fig. 20), and a doll with a head made by the Kestner Company about 1910 (fig. 21) indicate the variety.

Inside Springfield Dolls

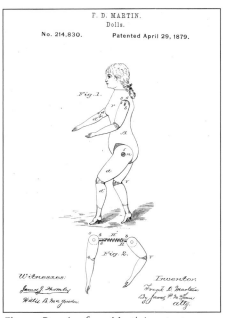

Fig. 22 *Drawing from Martin's patent*

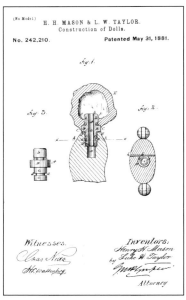

Fig. 23 *Mason and Taylor's patent drawing*

Toy makers in Springfield, Vermont, wrote five patents between 1873 and 1882 related to the manufacture of wood dolls. Patent 139130, written by Joel A. H. Ellis for the Co-operative Manufacturing Company, claimed the invention of a double tenon joint for knees and elbows and an innovation in the shoulder joint in which the end of the pin that creates the joint between the shoulder and arm is cut perpendicularly. Ellis dolls are easily separated from the dolls of later makers because the heads are invariably made of pressed maple.

The later papier-mâché-headed Springfield dolls are harder to distinguish from one another. In 1879 Frank D. Martin submitted his patent (U.S. patent 214830) for an improvement to the knee, elbow, and shoulder joints that uses hooks to secure the shoulders and half-globe joints at knees and elbows (fig. 22). In 1880 George W. Sanders submitted a patent for a half-round mortise-and-tenon joint for elbows and knees (U.S. patent 235300). Henry H. Mason and Luke W. Taylor created an improvement to the neck joint that prevented heads from falling off (U.S. patent 242210; approved 1881; fig. 23). In 1882 Charles C. Johnson patented his improvement on Mason and Taylor's neck joint which created a more durable head (U.S. patent 267212). By comparing radiographs to drawings from the Springfield patents, we have a better understanding of how early the dolls were made.[9]

One of the dolls in the collection appears to be an exact replica of George Martin's patent and could therefore be dated to about 1879 (20-5-117; fig. 24). The spring has released from the hook in the doll's right arm and is curled around the hook in the doll's left arm. The knees and elbows exhibit the half-ball joints secured with rivets shown in the patent drawing (see fig. 22).

Harder to discern in the x-radiographs is the distinction between the Mason and Taylor 1881 neck joint and the Johnson 1882 neck joint due to the x-ray-opaque lead-based paint that covers the papier-mâché heads and shoulders on three of Shelburne's dolls (figs. 24 and 25). As indicated in the patent, Mason and Taylor's neck joint was hollow, and none of the x-radiographs show the hollow in the joint.

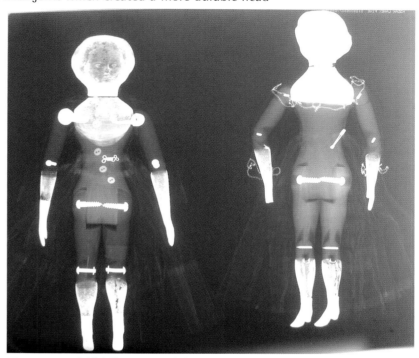

Fig. 24 *Springfield doll 20-5-121 on left and 20-5-117 on right. The doll on the right bears joinery depicted in Martin's patent. (See also fig. 42).*

The paint on the doll on the right side of figure 25 is the thinnest, and the radiograph of this doll shows that the neck peg on this doll is solid. A faint outline of the square wood core is evident at the top of the head within the hairline, which suggests that the doll has a Johnson neck. This fact dates the doll no earlier than 1882. All three dolls exhibit the Saunders half-round mortises at the knees and elbows, patented in 1880. The doll on the right side of figure 25 also has one surviving original wood pin in the left hip joint. The wood pin in the right hip has been replaced with a flat-headed wood screw, which unfortunately extends into the wood pin in the left hip.

With patents, radiographs, and microscopes, it is possible to show how the dolls were made, locate old repairs, and ascribe dates more securely. While technology is no substitute for good connoisseurship, it can be a useful partner to it.

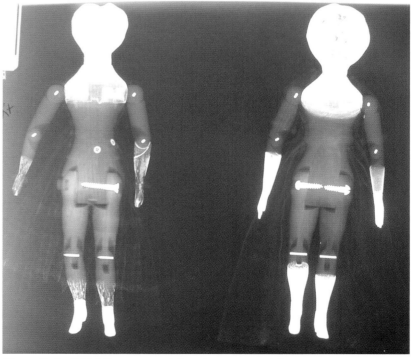

Fig. 25 *Springfield doll 20-5-119 on left and 20-5-120 on right*

Wooden Dolls

Inexpensive and readily available, wood is the earliest and longest-lasting material used for making dolls in Europe, the United States, and the Far East from about 1660 to 1950. Wooden dolls include rare, sophisticated, handmade masterpieces, numerous mass-produced models, and simple one-of-a-kind folk designs constructed by skilled but untrained artists. The Shelburne Museum collection encompasses English, German, American, and Chinese examples.

English Wooden (Queen Anne)

Most wooden dolls surviving from the 1600s and 1700s were made in England, probably in and around London by a number of unidentified professional carvers. English wooden dolls of this period are often called Queen Anne dolls—a misnomer—because most were made either before 1702 or after 1714, the years of her reign. Dating these rare, unmarked dolls is difficult and is based primarily on distinctive stylistic and construction features which include a turned and carved egg-shaped or round head and body made of pine and covered in gesso, paint, and varnish; glass almond-shaped or painted round eyes with dot-painted eyebrows; highly rouged cheeks and either cloth or carved limbs attached respectively with nails or mortise-and-tenon joints; and either oversized wooden fork- or smaller spatula-shaped hands.

Fig. 26
Detail of "Lady Betty Campbell"
England
1724
Written in brown ink on chemise: Lady Betty Campbell 1724
Carved wooden head and body with molded bosom, flat back and squared-off hips, brown human-hair wig, brown glass eyes, painted features, cloth upper arms, wooden fork-shaped fingers, wooden mortise-and-tenon joints at hips and knees, linen and silk costume, original chemise, corset, and stomacher
19"
10-11-98
Chandler Collection 1962-262.2

The individual facial variations on early eighteenth-century English dolls are clearly evident in "Lady Betty Campbell." She has a distinctive personality due to her downcast eyes and carved wooden nose. The whitish color of the facial painting reflects the contemporary fashion of using makeup to conceal facial imperfections.

The formal and fashionable clothing taught a child important skills such as how to dress oneself when putting on a piece of apparel such as a corset or stomacher in an incorrect order could have been uncomfortable or even painful to the wearer.[1] The corset constructed of heavy paper stitched to silk fabric is fitted around her molded bosom. It is laced up the back to provide the shape required to support the elaborate costumes of the day. The stomacher—visible in the center—is stitched to the corset and educated the body to sit and stand with correct posture. Both appear to be original to Lady Campbell.

Fig. 27
Lady
England
About 1720
Carved wooden head and body with molded bosom, flat back and squared-off hips, brown human-hair wig, brown glass eyes, painted features, cloth upper arms, wooden fork-shaped fingers, wooden mortise-and-tenon joints at hips and knees with hoof feet, embroidered linen dress
h 22 1/4"
20-11-87
Museum Purchase, 1957-510

Lady
England
Early Twentieth Century
Carved wooden head and body, flat back and squared-off hips, flax wig, brown teardrop-shaped glass eyes inserted in front of globe-shaped glass eyes, painted features, wooden limbs attached with globe joints, fork-shaped hands, dressed in old embroidered batiste costume with quilted slip in 1963
h 22 1/2"
20-11-118
Webb Collection, 1952-60

Lady
England
1724
Written in brown ink on chemise: Lady Betty Campbell 1724
Carved wooden head and body with molded bosom, flat back and squared-off hips, brown human- hair wig, brown glass eyes, painted features, cloth upper arms, wooden fork-shaped fingers, wooden mortise-and-tenon joints at hips and knees, linen and silk costume, original chemise, corset, and stomacher
h 19"
20-11-98
Chandler Collection, 1992-262.2

Stylistically, all three of these elegant English ladies share distinctive egg-shaped heads, large almond-shaped pupilless glass eyes with little white showing, and oversized, fork-shaped wooden hands. However, x-rays reveal the doll in the center has globe-shaped rather than mortise-and-tenon joints as well as two sets of eyes, one behind the other, making her an early twentieth-century fake. They are costumed in appropriate, old, but not original, dresses with embroidered stylized flowers, leaves, and vines with three-quarter-length sleeves fringed in lace. The quilted pockets, an essential component of eighteenth-century women's dress, served as purses containing those objects a lady of fashion deemed indispensable. Such a pocket tied around the waist from the back, "dropt from a Lady's Side," contained "Three Keys and a Seal on a String, and one larger single, a Pocket Knife, a Fan and about 20 guineas in gold and Silver loose."[2] "Lady Betty" (right) is also equipped with a woven ball suspended from her left side, possibly used to store her pins.

Fig. 28
Lady
England
About 1760
Carved wooden head and body, painted features, brown human-hair
wig, brown glass eyes, stick wooden arms with spatula hands, wood-
en mortise-and-tenon joints at hips with hoof feet, taffeta costume
remade from another old dress
h 12 ¹/₂"
20-11-88
Webb Collection, 1952-60

Lady
England
About 1750
Carved wooden head and body, brown human-hair wig, brown glass
eyes, painted features, wooden arms with spatula hands, wooden
mortise-and-tenon joints at hips with hoof feet, silk and cotton
clothing
h 14"
20-11-103
Webb Collection, 1952-60

Both of these elegant ladies have carved, stationary wooden heads, covered with gesso and paint, human-hair wigs, brown glass eyes with
dotted lashes and brows and brightly rouged cheeks. Carvers focused their attention on the facial features because the clothing obscured the
simple body, which consisted of one-piece legs ending in hoof feet, attached with mortise-and-tenon joints at the hips. The stick arms with
spatula hands are joined to the torso with string.

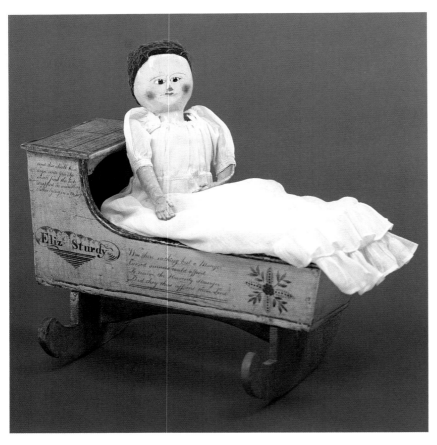

Fig. 29
Lady and Cradle
England
1800-1830
Carved wooden head and body, brown human-hair
wig, brown glass and porcelain eyes, cloth and kid
arms, legs missing
h 13"
Gift of Margaret Angier, 2002-1.2

Elizabeth Sturdy, the original owner, turned this
English lady into an infant by cutting her hair, removing her wooden legs, and placing her in this cradle, a
remarkable piece of folk art decorated with painting,
verses, and biblical inscriptions. According to family
history, after the death of her parents Elizabeth was
raised in an English convent, where she developed
her penmanship and artistic skills and decorated her
doll's cradle in the academic tradition of schoolgirl
art. Based on the subject matter of the verses, it is
possible to speculate that the infant doll she created
represented baby Jesus.

Figs. 30 & 31
Cradle
Written in brown script ink on proper right side:
And this shall be a sign unto you
Ye shall find the babe wrapped in swaddling
clothes lying in a manger
Was there nothing but a Manger
Cursed sinners could afford
To receive the Heavenly Stranger
Did they thus affront their Lord
Elizth Sturdy

Written in brown script ink on proper left side:
And there was in the same Country
shepherds abiding in the field
Keeping watch over their flock by night
Luke chap 2 vse 8
The flight of Joseph and Mary
with the child Jesus into Egypt

See the hinder shepherds round him
Telling wonders from the sky
Where they sought him there they found him
With his virgin Mother by

Written in brown ink at foot of cradle:
And when the woman saw that the
Tree was good for food, and that
It was pleasant to the eyes, and a
Tree to be desired to make one wise
She took of the fruit thereof and
Did eat and gat to her Husband

Fig. 32
Lady
England
1810-20
Carved wooden head, brown human-hair wig, brown glass eyes, painted features, rolled cotton arms, wooden body, one-piece mortise-and-tenon joints at hips with hoof feet, probably original polished cotton clothing and silk calash
h 10 3/4"
20-11-113
Webb Collection, 1952-60

This remarkable lady is distinguished by her original polished cotton pleated empire-style dress with puffed sleeves and stockings. The doll's padded feet are permanently stitched to the torso and legs respectively, as are the silk scarf (calash) and bonnet. Her unusually pale face might be attributed to the fact that barium sulfate—introduced as a pigment in 1782 and commercially available about 1810—has been identified in the paint layer. It was perhaps used intentionally to imitate the fashion of the period.

Fig. 33
Lady
England
About 1800
Turned wooden head, brown cloth hair, painted features, wooden body, rolled cloth arms, no legs, silk costume
h 9 1/2"
20-11-140
Gift of Allen B. Harbach, 1991-11.1

Lady
England
About 1820
Turned wooden head, brown human-hair wig, painted features, cloth arms with no hands, wooden body with flat splint legs, wired joints, silk costume
h 10 1/2"
20-11-131
Gift of Alice Grant, 1967-40

These two English wooden dolls are typical of early nineteenth-century designs with painted rather than glass eyes, round rather than egg-shaped faces, and less distinctive expressions. They each have one-piece pointed rather than square-bottomed bodies and old cloth instead of the eighteenth-century wooden arms with carved hands.

Fig. 34
"Lady Teazle"
England
About 1930
Turned wooden head and body, brown animal-hair wig, blue glass paperweight eyes, painted features, wooden arms attached at joints with cloth, carved spatula hands, wooden mortise-and-tenon joints at hips and knees, feet missing, original silk costume
h 33"
20-11-86
Webb Collection 1952-60, formerly in the collection of the Victoria and Albert Museum, London

Unlike her stately predecessors, this English novelty doll was created to celebrate Richard Sheridan's comedy play on manners entitled "School for Scandal," first produced in Drury Lane in 1777. This character, entitled "Lady Teazle," is closely related to several others depicted in this play, Mrs. Candor and Lady Sneerwell, currently in the collections of the Victoria and Albert and Bethnal Green Museums in London. Originally thought to be period, they are now considered twentieth-century fakes, made about 1930.[3] They all have an imposing stature, beautiful silk brocade dresses, startling glass paperweight eyes, and towering powdered animal hair coiffures. The fearful and fanciful hairdo is a topknot called a fontanage—an elaborate tiered ruffle affair fastened to a wire frame headdress and popular for French women in the 1690s. According to James Laver, the style was named "after one of Louis XIV of France's favorites, Mme de Fontanage who, finding her hair disarrayed while hunting, hastily tied it up with one of her garters. The King expressed his admiration and next day all the Court ladies appeared with their hair tied with a ribbon and a bow in front." This unusual fashion quickly crossed the Channel and became the rage almost immediately in England.[4]

German Wooden Dolls
Penny woodens, Dutch dolls, Peg woodens

From the end of the eighteenth-century, cheaper German dolls (hence the name "penny," referring to the cost per dozen) competed with the expensive English models. The word Dutch may be a corruption of Deutsch, meaning German, indicating their country of origin, or it may be a reference to the Dutch ports through which they were exported in volume from Germany to England. The term "peg" refers to the use of small wooden pins in the jointing of all the limbs assembled either with ball and socket or mortise and tenons on the large and small dolls respectively. The resulting flexibility at shoulders, elbows, hips, and knees allowed them to assume many different poses. Regardless of terminology, all of these dolls, ranging in height from one to forty inches, are simple, all-wooden figures.

Peasants in the Grödner Tal (once Germany, but now an area of Northern Italy in the Alps) carved the one-piece pine head and torso, hand painted and varnished the exposed parts and dressed these dolls during the harsh winter months when they could not work in the forests. They worked in a highly specialized cottage industry in which they made dolls by hand, step by step, in the rural outlying areas and then sold them through distributors in large cities such as Sonneburg or Nürnberg. Distributors exported them in voluminous quantity to England and beyond. This type of doll was the favorite of Queen Victoria, who as a child and a young woman collected one hundred of them, which are currently on loan to the Museum of London from Kensington Palace.

Fig. 35
Lady
Germany
About 1825
Carved wooden head and body with molded bosom, carved and painted features, wooden arms and legs with pegged mortise-and-tenon joints, voile dress
16 3/4"
0-11-105
Webb Collection, 1952-60

The early Grödner Tal dolls, like this one, were carved and painted with a great deal of attention given to details. Although made in quantity, each doll has its own special features. This lady's identity is defined by her hairstyle—the absence of a center part determines her sex—and the fine brush marks framing her face soften her expression. The exceptional modeling is evident in the carved exposed ears, three-dimensional nose, oversized hands with four molded fingers, separate thumb, knuckles, and even fingernails.

Fig. 36
Tuck Comb Lady
Germany
About 1825
Carved wooden head and body with molded bosom, carved and painted features, wooden arms and legs with pegged mortise-and-tenon joints and spatula hands, cotton dress
h 13 1/4"
20-11-108
Webb Collection, 1952-60

Tuck Comb Lady
Germany
About 1820
Turned wooden head and body, carved and painted features, ears pierced into head with amethyst glass earrings, wooden arms and legs with pegged mortise-and-tenon joints and spatula hands, silk dress
h 14 5/8"
20-11-107
Webb Collection, 1952-60

Tuck Comb Lady
Germany
About 1810
Turned wooden head and body, carved and painted features, wooden arms and legs with pegged mortise- and-tenon joints, cotton dress
h 7 1/2"
20-11-55
Webb Collection, 1952-60

Tuck Comb Lady
Germany
About 1830
Carved wooden head and body, carved and painted features, wooden arms and legs with pegged mortise- and-tenon joints and spatula hands, crépeline dress and cotton underwear
h 10 1/2"
20-11-30
Webb Collection, 1952-60

Tuck Comb Lady
Germany
About 1830
Carved wooden head and body with molded bosom, painted features, glass bead earrings, wooden arms and legs with pegged mortise- and-tenon joints and spatula hands, original taffeta dress
h 11"
20-11-114
Webb Collection, 1952-60

Tuck Comb Lady
Germany
About 1810
Turned wooden head and jointed body with molded bosom, carved and painted features, beaded necklace, wooden arms and legs with pegged mortise-and-tenon joints and spatula hands, cotton dress
h 10 1/2"
20-11-38
Webb Collection, 1952-60

Tuck Comb Lady
Germany
About 1825
Turned wooden head and body, carved and painted features, wool dress
h 14 3/4"
20-11-116
Webb Collection, 1952-60

Most of these ladies share a carved yellow comb crowning the head, giving them the popular name of "tuck comb." The Grödner Tal dolls were designed to represent women with elongated necks, carved waists, and defined bosoms accentuated by high-waisted empire-style gowns. The hair is indicated by a painted black pate that is outlined at the temple with wispy, brush-marked gray tendrils. Exceptions are found in the doll at left (20-11-108) with carved hair in the rear and the doll at center (20-11-30) with a coiffure of high raised loops known as the Apollo's knot, usually reserved for papier-mâché dolls of the 1830s. Painting—straight on the wood without the base gesso layer—is reserved for the head, neck, lower arms, hands, and lower legs. Since other body parts are covered with clothing, their thrifty makers saved time and money by leaving them unpainted. As a result, these dolls were less expensive than the English "Queen Ann" woodens. Spoon-shaped wooden hands and flat wooden feet with painted slippers are ubiquitous features of early peg-wooden dolls.

Fig. 37
Peg-Wooden Lady
Germany
About 1850
Turned wooden head and body, painted features, wooden arms and legs with pegged mortise-and-tenon joints and spatula hands, original cotton clothing
h 8 ½"
20-11-56
Webb Collection, 1952-60

Reproduction Peg-Wooden Lady
Gift of William Fifer, 2003

Peg-Wooden Lady
Germany
About 1810
Turned wooden head, carved and painted features, black mohair wig, bead earrings, wooden arms and legs with pegged mortise-and-tenon joints, original silk dress with beads
h 6"
20-11-50
Webb Collection, 1952-60

Both of these fashionably dressed ladies have extremely narrow waists accentuated by their period-style costumes. The doll on the left also has "leg of mutton"-shaped sleeves typical of the 1830s, while her companion is remarkable for her wig of tight mohair curls topped with a carved beaded comb—an unusual combination. The flexibility of the pinned mortise-and-tenon joints, evident in their undressed companion, and their small size, explains why peg woodens were popular dollhouse inhabitants of the time.

Fig. 38
Peddler Lady
Germany
About 1840
Turned wooden head and body, painted features, wooden limbs with pegged mortise-and-tenon joints, polished cotton clothing, wicker tray with wares
h 9 3/4"
20-07-10
Webb Collection, 1952-60

Peg woodens were often used to create peddler dolls, carrying a basket overflowing with miniature wares, such as buttons and thread, dustpan with brush, cards, books, and even dolls. Given a prominent place on a fashionable Victorian drawing room mantelpiece or whatnot and usually sitting beneath a glass dome to protect it from dust, this conversation piece was clearly designed for adults rather than children. Most peddler dolls were made in Germany but dressed in England by professional or individual craftsmen. The heads were often wood, but wax and kid were also used.

Fig. 39
Lady
Germany
About 1850
Carved wooden shoulder head, carved painted black hair with center part and coiled braids at side and bun at rear, painted features, cloth swing-jointed body, leather arms with separate fingers, cotton walking suit, black velvet high-heeled shoes
h 21 1/2"
20-11-126
Webb Collection, 1952-60

Lady
Germany
About 1850
Carved wooden shoulder head, carved painted black hair with center part and bun at back, painted features, cloth unjointed body with wooden lower arms, cotton dress
h 23"
20-11-26
Webb Collection, 1952-60

Girl
Germany
About 1850
Stamped in black ink on inside proper right thigh: illegible mark
Carved wooden shoulder head, carved black hair with part on proper left, painted features, unjointed kid body with wooden lower limbs, cotton dress
h 24 1/2"
20-11-125
Webb Collection, 1952-60

These three German dolls are distinguished by their three-dimensional hairstyles which are elaborately carved on front, side, and back with spit curls, buns, and coiled braids. Instead of the all-wooden jointed bodies found on peg woodens, these are made of either cloth or kid.

Fig. 40
Peg-Wooden Lady
Germany
About 1880
Carved wooden head and body, carved and painted
features, wooden stump arms and legs attached with
kid, cotton costume
H 8 ¹/₂"
20-11-110
Webb Collection, 1952-60

Peg-Wooden Lady with Two Babies
Germany
About 1850
Carved wooden heads and bodies, carved and painted
features, wooden arms and legs with pegged mortise-
and-tenon joints, cotton dresses
H 10 ¹/₂"
20-11-99
Museum Purchase, 1962-174

Peg-Wooden Lady
Germany
About 1880
Carved wooden head and body, carved and painted
features, wooden stump arms attached with kid, cot-
ton voile dress
H 9"
20-11-111
Webb Collection, 1952-60

Fig. 41
Peg-Wooden Lady
Germany
About 1840
Turned wooden head and body, painted features,
wooden arms and legs with mortise-and-tenon joints,
redressed in cotton paisley, with original cotton
underclothing
H 21 ³/₄"
20-11-90
Chandler Collection, 1962-242.4

This grouping of peg woodens characterized by
squarer-shaped heads and shorter necks range in size
from adult women to small babies produced from
about 1840 to 1890. However, all have the same
petite features clustered in the center of the face and
placed low so that a high forehead results. Stylized
features include blue or black dot-on-dot eyes set
wide apart with upper eyeliner, single-stroke black
brows, minimally carved noses with accented nostrils,
tiny closed mouths painted red, and blush spots on
cheeks. The later examples are characterized by
abbreviated stump arms attached with kid rather than
joinery techniques, and fewer carved and painted
facial details.

American Wooden
Springfield Woodens

In the United States, New England was the creative center for toy and doll making in the mid-nineteenth century. Although European wooden doll production was virtually nonexistent by 1880, a small but innovative industry began anew in Vermont in 1873. Taking advantage of local maple wood and showing an interest in German ingenuity (articulated joints), an enterprising group of independent entrepreneurs—including Joel Ellis, George Sanders, Frank Martin, Henry Mason and Luke Taylor, and Charles Johnson—patented a number of doll improvements featuring intricate limb jointing. Because human partners changed companies and doll parts were interchanged from 1873 to 1893, identifying any particular doll as to maker and patent has, in the past, presented a challenge and has resulted in the use of the generic term "Springfield Wooden" to define the type. However, using x-ray techniques, the Shelburne Museum in cooperation with Fletcher Allen Health Center in Burlington, Vermont, has been able to identify internal patented mechanisms and more accurately attribute individual dolls in this category.

Fig. 42
Lady
Springfield, Vermont, United States
Attributed to Jointed Doll Co.
1874-85
Composition over wooden head with swivel neck, molded and painted features,
wooden body and limbs with both mortise-and-tenon and pinned ball-and-socket joints,
metal lower arms and legs
11 1/2"
0-05-117
Webb Collection, 1952-60

X-ray examination reveals this Springfield wooden is an exact replica of George Martin's 1879 patent (see fig. 22) featuring half-globe joints secured with rivets at elbows and knees and a metal hook and spring assembly to connect the arms to the shoulder sockets. The doll is also equipped with the composition-over-core wood head patented by Charles Johnson of Springfield in 1882. To make the head, a mixture of rye flour and glue was combined, rolled out, and cut into two circles which were placed on either side of a wooden core and shaped in a press. Many of these dolls were sold undressed.

Fig. 43
Girl
Springfield, Vermont, United States
Joel Ellis, Cooperative Manufacturing Co.
1873-74
Maple swivel head and body, molded and
painted features, wooden limbs with mortise-and-tenon joints, pewter hands and feet
h 12"
20-11-12
Webb Collection, 1952-60

Gentleman
Probably United States
About 1880
Carved wooden head and body, carved and
painted features, wooden arms and legs
with pegged mortise- and-tenon joints
h 12"
20-11-24
Webb Collection, 1952-60

Gentleman
United States
About 1880
Carved one-piece wooden head and body,
carved and painted features, turned arms
and legs with pinned mortise-and-tenon
joints, wool costume
h 13"
20-11-25
Webb Collection, 1952-60

This remarkable grouping of all-wooden dolls share molded or carved hair and flexible limb articulation, but here the similarity ends.
Claiming the invention of a double tenon joint for knees and elbows held together by steel pins, Joel Ellis patented the doll at left on May 2o
1872. Functionally, the joints allowed complete range of movement and permitted posing—a design that led advertisers to declare that the
"care and trouble of dressing" the doll could be avoided. The green rock maple heads were cut in a cube, steamed, and then shaped in a
hydraulic press with steel dies to form the features. Women, who made up one-third of the Cooperative Manufacturing Company's sixty
employees, painted the dolls' hair, facial features, and pewter hands and feet. The dolls were sold undressed. Pewter was not new to doll
manufacture; it had been used on marionettes to give weight to the hands and feet. Although Ellis stopped making the dolls after a fire
destroyed his factory, the Vermont Novelty Works in Springfield subsequently manufactured them until 1893.

Fig. 44
Girl
Springfield, Vermont, United States
Attributed to Jointed Doll Co.
1874-85
Swivel composition over wooden core head,
molded and painted features, pressed and
molded paper (Dresden) around neck to conceal swivel joint, black paper band around
middle, wooden body with both mortise-
and-tenon and pinned ball-and-socket joints,
upper arms and legs, metal lower arms and
legs, velvet and lace dress
h 12"
20-05-119
Webb Collection, 1952-60

Girl
Springfield, Vermont, United States
Attributed to Jointed Doll Co.
1874-85
Swivel composition over wooden core head,
molded and painted features, wooden body
with both mortise- and-tenon and pinned
ball-and-socket joints, wooden lower arms,
metal lower legs, cotton dress
h 11 1/2"
20-05-120
Webb Collection, 1952-60

Girl
Springfield, Vermont, United States
Attributed to Jointed Doll Co.
1874-85
Swivel composition over wooden core head,
molded and painted features, wooden body
with both mortise-and-tenon and pinned
ball-and-socket joints, wooden lower arms,
metal lower legs
h 11 3/4"
20-05-121
Webb Collection, 1952-60

...rays reveal a combination of several innovative inventions by the collaborative group of men in Vermont. They all exhibit the half-round mortise-and-tenon joints at knees and elbows described in George Sanders's 1880 patent (no. 235,300) as well as the composition-over-wooden-core head in Charles Johnson's 1882 patent. In addition, the girl at left (20-05-119) has the 1873 Joel Ellis shoulder articulation in which the end of the socket is cut with two perpendicular kerfs to prevent the joint from binding (patent no. 139,130). The dolls at center and right illustrate Henry Mason and Luke Taylor's improved hollow neck joint which permits the head to rotate (patent no. 242,210). (See fig. 23).

American Wooden Dolls
by Albert Schoenhut

Albert Schoenhut (1872-about 1925)—the third generation of a German toy-making family—carried the European woodworking tradition to America when he immigrated to Philadelphia in 1866. Here he established his own company in 1872 and produced, among other things, toy pianos, doll houses, circus figures, and his Perfection Art Doll. Patented in 1911, this wooden jointed wonder with steel springs, affording flexible positioning, was a marvel of workmanship and of practically indestructible design. When a child pulled on its joints, the springs would compress rather than stretch, thus extending the life of the doll. The bodies were lathe-turned, and the heads were machine carved from solid basswood and enhanced by hand carved accents before finishing by hot molding under pressure. The facial features were painted by hand. The dolls produced by Schoenhut's company until the 1930s exhibit a variety of eye treatments, carved hairstyles, or separate wigs, but all depict real children with lifelike expressions. Patented, poseable, and playable, the Schoenhut dolls represent the early twentieth century's foremost American wooden doll.

fig. 45
irl
iladelphia, Pennsylvania, United States
bert Schoenhut & Co.
bout 1911
aper decal on back: Schoenhut Doll/Pat. Jan 11 th 1911/U.S.A.
arved and molded wooden socket head, brown mohair wig, brown intaglio eyes,
ainted features, steel-spring-jointed wooden body and limbs, cotton dress,
raw hat
18 ¹/₂"
)-11-122
useum Purchase, 1955-635.1

ie dolls produced by Schoenhut's company until the 1930s exhibit carved or applied hair, a variety of eye treatments, and either dolly or aracter faces. This young girl with mohair wig and chubby cheeks has hollow (intaglio) eyes—with the iris and pupil carved and then essed in the mold and finally painted—creating a distinctive concave surface and lifelike expression.

Fig. 46
Baby
Philadelphia, Pennsylvania,
United States
Albert Schoenhut & Co.
About 1913
Paper decal on back of neck: H.
E. Schoenhut
Paper decal on back: Schoenhut
Doll Pat. Jan. 17. 1911, U.S.A.
Carved and molded wooden
socket head, brown mohair wig,
painted features, five-piece-bent
limb wooden body
h 15"
20-11-123
Museum Purchase, 1955-635.3

Girl
Philadelphia, Pennsylvania,
United States
Albert Schoenhut & Co.
About 1911
Paper decal on back: Schoenhut
Doll/Pat. Jan 17th 1911/U.S.A.
Carved and molded wooden
socket head, mohair wig, decal
eyes, painted features,
open/closed mouth with teeth,
steel-spring-jointed wooden
body and limbs, cotton dress
h 16 ¹/₂"
20-11-121
Museum Purchase, 1955-635.2

Girl
Philadelphia, Pennsylvania,
United States
Albert Schoenhut & Co.
Paper decal on back: Schoenhut
Doll/Pat. Jan 11 th 1911/U.S.A.
About 1911
Carved and molded wooden
socket head, brown mohair wig,
brown intaglio eyes, painted fea-
tures, steel-spring-jointed wood-
en body and limbs, cotton dress,
straw hat
h 18 ¹/₂"
20-11-122
Museum Purchase, 1955-635.1

Boy
Philadelphia, Pennsylvania,
United States
Albert Schoenhut & Co.
About 1911
Paper decal on back: Schoenhu
Doll/Pat. Jan 11th 1911/U.S.A.
Carved and molded wooden
socket head, blonde mohair wig
blue intaglio eyes, painted fea-
tures, steel-spring-jointed wood
body and limbs
h 19 ¹/₂"
20-11-92
Chandler Collection, 1962-262.

These dolls illustrate Albert Schoenhut's unique steel-spring jointing system patented in 1911, which allows movement but is rigid enough t
hold the doll in position without falling. The articulated wooden child body can be posed through holes in the feet (20-11- 92) designed to f
into projecting pins in a specially built metal stand. However, this varied product line also includes toddlers and infants of both sexes. The
boy and the girl on the right both have character faces with individual personalities. The kneeling dolly-faced girl has a five-piece bent-limb
body.

Fig. 47
Pennsylvania German Lady
United States
About 1840
Wooden shoulder head, painted
features, cloth body, wooden
limbs attached with paper
bands, redressed in old clothing
by Marta Mengis in 1961
h 24"
20-05-102
Chandler Collection, 1962-
62.42

Lady
United States
About 1820
Written in pencil on back shoulder: March 1820
Wooden head and body to
waist, carved and painted features, cloth lower body, cloth
swing-jointed lower arms and
legs, cotton dress
h 19 ½"
20-11-36
Webb Collection, 1952-60

Gentleman Jim Corbett
United States
About 1890
Written in ink on back of neck:
Gentleman Jim Corbett
Stamped on body: Chicago, St.
Louis, Milwaukee Bag Co.
Wooden head, carved and
painted features, sacking body,
cloth upper and lower limbs,
carved wooden hands and feet
h 23 ½"
20-11-130
Museum Collection 2004-8

Fig. 48
Abraham Lincoln
United States
About 1860
Wooden nodding head, carved
and painted features, wooden
body
h 10 ¼"
20-11-23
Webb Collection, 1952-60

Girl
Probably United States
1800-1850
Wooden shoulder head, painted
features, cloth body, carved
wooden limbs, cotton clothing
h 9"
20-11-20
Webb Collection, 1952-60

While this diverse group of five individually made dolls all have
hand-carved wooden heads, each one is a unique folk art creation.
They represent men, women, and children of various ethnic groups,
and probably all originated in the United States during the nineteenth century.

Chinese Wooden Dolls
Door of Hope Dolls

The European doll-making tradition was transplanted to Asia in the twentieth century. It was a popular practice for foreign missionaries around the world to encourage native craftsmen to create dolls that depicted representative members of their societies. From about 1900 to 1950 almost all the dolls in mainland China were assembled, dressed, and sold in Protestant missions established at Shanghai and Canton to assist destitute and abandoned children. Designed as attractive souvenirs for sale to raise funds to support their charity work, they were made on site and distributed through representatives in China, England, Australia, the United States, and South Africa. The dolls accurately depict aspects of the culture of the country with carefully carved pearwood heads and cloth bodies dressed in elaborate, removeable, handmade costumes.

Fig. 49
Cantonese Amah and Baby
Shanghai, China
Door of Hope Mission
About 1902
Carved swivel pearwood head, carved and painted features, cloth body, cotton costume
11" (adult), 5 1/4" (child)
LO-O3-137C
Webb Collection, 1952-60

This Amah or nursemaid with her charge was an indispensable figure in well-regulated Chinese households. The natural color of their pearwood heads resembles the ivory complexion of the Chinese skin. The heads were probably carved by men from nearby Ningpo. Touches of paint were added for the lips, eyes, and hair, all without varnish.

Fig. 50
Bridegroom
Shanghai, China
Door of Hope Mission
About 1902 (prior to 1914)
Carved swivel pearwood head, carved and
painted features, cloth body, silk costume
h 12"
20-03-137h
Webb Collection, 1952-60

Bride
Shanghai, China
Door of Hope Mission
About 1902 (prior to 1914)
Carved swivel pearwood head, carved and
painted features, cloth body, silk costume,
headdress missing
h 12"
20-03-137g
Webb Collection, 1952-60

As red is the Chinese color of hope and new
life, this bride wears the brightest scarlet silk
with elaborate tucks and embroidery. The
groom is similarly decked out in silk in a
more somber hue, with high boots.

Young Lady
Shanghai, China
Door of Hope Mission
About 1902
Carved swivel pearwood head, carved and
painted features, cloth body, silk costume,
missing headdress
h 12"
20-03-137b
Webb Collection, 1952-160

Manchu Woman
Shanghai, China
Door of Hope Mission
Prior to 1914
Carved swivel pearwood head, carved and
painted features, cloth body, silk costume
h 15"
Museum Collection, 2004-9.3

School Boy
Shanghai, China
Door of Hope Mission
1902-1940
Carved swivel pearwood head, carved and
painted features, cloth body, silk costume
h 12"
Museum Collection, 2004-9.2

Municipal Policeman
Shanghai, China
Door of Hope Mission
Prior to 1914
Carved swivel pearwood head, carved and
painted features, cloth body, wool clothing
h 12"
Museum Collection, 2004-9.5

These men, women, and children represent
some of the twenty-five standard Door of
Hope characters meant to illustrate a broad
panorama of social levels and occupations.
The cloth stuffed bodies and clothes were
sewn by the women at the mission.
Instructed in exquisite needlework, each
young girl working five days a week meticulously constructed only one doll a month.
The garments are appropriate to each character and include intricate frog closures,
elaborate headdress, and appropriate
footwear.

Fig. 51
Mourner
Shanghai, China
Door of Hope Mission
About 1902
Carved swivel pearwood head, carved and
painted features, cloth body, muslin and
sackcloth robe, cloth slippers
h 12"
20-03-137a
Webb Collection, 1952-1960

Buddhist Priest
Shanghai, China
Door of Hope Mission
1902-40
Carved swivel pearwood head, carved and
painted features, cloth body, padded cotton
robe, cotton slippers
h 12"
Museum Collection, 2004-9.4

Widow
Shanghai, China
Door of Hope Mission
About 1902
Carved swivel pearwood head, carved and
painted features, cloth body, muslin and
sackcloth costume
h 12"
20-03-137d
Webb Collection, 1952-60

Cantonese Amah and Baby
Shanghai, China
Door of Hope Mission
About 1902
Carved swivel pearwood head, carved and
painted features, cloth body, cotton costume
h 11" (adult), 5 1/4" (child)
20-03-137c
Webb Collection, 1952-60

Woman Amah
Shanghai, China
Door of Hope Mission
1902-40
Carved swivel pearwood head, carved and
painted features, cloth body, cotton costume
h 12"
Museum Collection, 2004-9.6

Chang the Chinese Farmer
Shanghai, China
Door of Hope Mission
About 1902
Carved swivel pearwood head, carved and
painted features, cloth body, cotton and
straw costume with coolie hat
h 9 1/2"
20-03-137e
Webb Collection, 1952-60

Chinese people of all ages, social levels, and occupations were faithfully and faultlessly portrayed in these dolls, down to the smallest detail. The mourner carries a wand of rags for driving off evil spirits. The priest has nine circles on top of his head to represent Buddhist scars formed by little charcoal coals smoldering on the pate. The Amah Chinese nursemaid wears the blue cotton of her class. The baby on her back is fitted with shoes shaped at the toes like a cat's head to help him walk through life as softly as a cat does. The Chinese farmer with broad brimmed coolie hat wears his straw raincoat and rake tucked into his belt.

Papier-Mâché Dolls

Papier-mâché—which literally means "chewed paper" in French—is a material that was widespread in Asia long before the Europeans began to work with it. In China molded paper pulp was used as a support for lacquer since about 600 AD before coming to England for applied decoration in architecture (plasterwork) and cabinetmaking (furniture) in the late seventeenth century. Due to its strength, malleability, and versatility, it was eventually employed for buttons, ornaments, boxes, and, of course, dolls heads and bodies as a substitute for wood. It could be poured into a mold in order to reproduce exactly a predetermined pattern—a process which eliminated labor-intensive hand-carving techniques.

The basic ingredients for papier mâché include shredded, beaten, or mashed paper pulp (a byproduct of the burgeoning book industry in eighteenth-century Germany) soaked with water and heated to a boil; fillers such as flour, sand, clay or chalk to add stability; and binders, which include animal glue, starch-paste, or gum Arabic, to hold the resulting dough together. In addition, the mixture may contain various additives such as rags, eggshells, or crushed bones to increase the stability and reduce the cost of the product. Some manufacturers added resins, oils, and other repellents to make the dolls less desirable to rodents; others added deodorizers to minimize the odors of the glue. In any event, the makers developed their own recipes and formulas which were closely guarded secrets. The term papier mâché is often used interchangeably with the word composition. However, throughout this text composition will be reserved for all papier-mâché heads made in the last quarter of the nineteenth century, which contain less pulp in proportion to more dense filler and binder.

continued on next page

Fig. 52
Detail of Lady
Germany
about 1830
papier-mâché shoulder head with unusual blue painted band around the edges, molded painted black hair, painted features, unjointed kid body stuffed with sawdust with carved wooden limbs, glued junction covered with red paper bands, blue painted slippers
17"
0-05-20
Webb Collection, 1952-60

This elegant papier-mâché lady mirrors the physical characteristics of an adult with her oval face, long neck, and deep shoulder plate with molded bosom. Typical German painted features include the striking Prussian blue eyes, with brown eyeliner and brows, accented nostrils, and highly rouged cheeks. From the beginning of the nineteenth century many women applied cosmetics generously, and one London author writing in 1825 argued strongly in favor of rouge. He asked, "In an age when women blush so little ought we not to value this innocent article which is capable of now and then exhibiting to us at least the picture of modesty?"[1]

Fig. 53
Production of Papier-Mâché Dolls
Copper Engraving from Christoff Weigel (Regensburg, 1698)
Courtesy Christiane Gräfnitz, *Papier-Mâché Dolls* (1994)

This change occurred in order to simulate the more fashionable, but more breakable, bisque.

The production of the papier-mâché heads involved a number of specialized skills. Unfortunately, the sculptors, mold makers, and painters cannot be identified because they rarely, if ever, left their mark on the finished product. The sculptor or modeler carved the original pattern of the head out of clay to form the master. The mold maker poured plaster of paris over the master to produce a negative version of the original. The papier-mâché dough was mixed according to formula and then pressed into the disassembled front and back sections of the mold and allowed to harden in the sun or in a well-heated room. Once dry, the resulting face masks were removed, trimmed, and assembled with cabinetmaker's hide glue. The finishing process was twofold and involved painting the skin and facial features with various pigments mixed with glue, followed by the application of a turpentine-based varnish.

The factories making these dolls needed to be near paper mills to have easy access to their primary raw materials, which led to the establishment of certain important areas of manufacture in Germany, such as Sonneberg. The first reliable reference to playthings made of paper pulp is found in a document published in 1698 which describes the "paper toy makers":

> Toys and dolls are things which children love playing with very much, much more than a miser loves money or gold. One is able to persuade a tender youth to all sorts of things when they are bribed with dolls and toys. . . . The various toy items can also be useful to observe youthful habits and find out what they are most interested in . . . Some are made in such a way that they encourage little maids and young girls to copy all the kind of work done in the household and in the kitchen, and this gradually prepares them for all kinds of useful pursuits in their adult lives. . . . These give pleasure not only to the children but also to adults who enjoy watching the children at play. We don't want to waste too much time on them though, and leave these childish playthings to the children themselves.[2]

Whether used to bribe, teach, or amuse children as well as adults, the function of papier-mâché dolls was clearly understood. As early as 1805, Johann Friedrich Muller was given the exclusive right to manufacture and sell papier-mâché goods in Sonneberg, Germany, and is credited with the first mass-production and distribution of this material for doll heads. Many writers describe the Sonneberg Merchant, the verleger, as one who pirated designs, undercut prices, and exploited workers and their small children.[3] The role of these trained businessmen was to market the products of numerous German factories to various countries and to guide their respective city's production into the most lucrative commercial ventures. This distribution system was instituted by ducal privilege and granted exclusively to twenty-seven merchants who had exclusive right to trade internationally. Independent family businesses bought their own ingredients, invested in materials, and sold their half-finished product—wigged heads or dressed bodies—to the doll assembling factory either at their own risk or under contract to one particular factory. From the industry's inception, Germany produced most of the papier-mâché doll heads for local sale as well as for export to other parts of Europe as well as to America. With rare exceptions, German doll heads are not marked but can be dated in a broad sense based on hairstyles, which copied contemporary fashions and were sometimes named after such famous royalty as Princess Adelaide of Germany, whose husband, King William IV of Great Britain, ruled from 1830 to 1837, or Queen Victoria f England, in power from 1837 to 1901. German firms also exported a large number of heads to France where they ere put on French bodies, dressed by Frenchwomen, and sold as French dolls. The dolls produced in Sonneberg are apier-mâché shoulder heads (consisting of head, neck, chest, and upper back) glued onto unjointed, narrow-waist-d, two-part kid bodies stitched up the front with carved lower wooden arms and legs. The glued junction between e kid upper and wooden lower limbs is covered with colored bands of paper. They have spoon-shaped hands and ainted shoes on flat feet and are tightly stuffed with sawdust (See fig. 55.) Collectors have referred to these dolls as milliner models," a misleading term because they were not models but dolls and usually play dolls, sometimes for dults as well as for children. The closest association many of them had with a milliner was in their clothing, which as professionally made.

owever, there are other variants to this manufactured kid body which include an all-cloth manufactured version, inted at knee and hip; French fashion bodies with three-seam seats and gusseted joints (see fig. 133 in Bisque ction), two-piece front and back cloth bodies, as well as a variety of homemade, hand-sewn, or even hand-carved odies.

he foremost manufacturers of papier-mâché dolls in America were, not surprisingly, German immigrants who brought eir skills and supplies with them to this country. Philip Lerch (active from 1858 to about 1875) and Ludwig Greiner who received the first doll patent in the United States for reinforcing his papier-mâché heads with cloth in 1858), ttled in Philadelphia, one of the largest textile cities in the world. All of the essential raw materials for a toy manu-cturer and merchant were available there, including mills supplying paper, plaster companies making chemicals for loring, and varnish manufacturers, as well as twill and leather for doll bodies and animal hair for stuffing. eads were either sold separately for cloth bodies made at home or attached to bodies that other Philadelphia anufacturers produced. Furthermore, an eager buying public existed because German dolls and heads of papier-âché and later china and bisque dominated American markets until orld War 1.

though papier-mâché dolls were made throughout the nineteenth entury, the Shelburne collection is particularly strong in German, ench, and American examples dating from 1820 to 1860—the most novative and varied period of their production.

g. 54
dy
ermany
bout 1820
apier-mâché shoulder head, molded painted black hair, painted features, unjoint-d kid body with carved wooden lower limbs, glued junction covered with red ather bands, spoon hands and red painted boots, old cotton dress, cotton pan-lets, petticoat, and chemise
22 1/4"
-05-78
ebb Collection, 1952-60

ecause many of the papier-mâché dolls have modeled hair, they provide an structive view of changing fashions and styles. This doll's remarkable coiffure nsists of three-dimensional curls on either side of the face and is pulled up on p into a high braided coronet with a large "Spanish" comb in back and fine inted brush marks around the face. Unusually, the mold line for her head runs wn the back and along the sides of the face, indicating that a three- rather than o-part mold was used, perhaps to accommodate the modeling of her elaborate irdo. Her coiffure is complimented by the high-waisted empire-style dress with iffed sleeves, which is very appropriate for the period.

Fig. 55
Lady
Germany
About 1830
Papier-mâché shoulder head,
molded painted black hair, painted features, kid swing-jointed
body with carved wooden lower
limbs, glued junction covered
with paper bands, old silk dress
h 24 ¹/₂"
20-05-37
Webb Collection, 1952-60

Lady
Germany
About 1830
Papier-mâché shoulder head,
molded painted black hair, painted features, unjointed kid body
with carved wooden lower limbs,
glued junction covered with
paper bands
h 17"
20-05-20
Webb Collection, 1952-60

Lady
Germany
About 1830
Papier-mâché shoulder head,
molded painted black hair, painted features, unjointed kid body
with carved wooden lower limbs,
glued junction covered with
paper bands, silk dress
h 9 ¹/₂"
20-11-33
Webb Collection, 1952-60

Lady
Germany
About 1830
Papier-mâché shoulder head,
molded painted black hair, painted features, unjointed kid body
with carved wooden lower limbs,
glued junction covered with
paper bands, original mull costume and cotton undergarments
h 15 ¹/₂'"
20-05-19
Webb Collection, 1952-60

Lady
Germany
About 1830
Papier-mâché shoulder head,
molded painted black hair, painted features, unjointed kid body
with carved wooden lower limbs,
glued junction covered with
paper bands, original silk girl's
dress
h 22"
20-05-39
Webb Collection, 1952-60

During the 1830s women's hairstyles were fantastic. The coiffure was dressed very high on
top of the head with elaborate
knots, swirls, and braids and
decorated with beads, feathers,
and flowers. In addition to
spreading upward, it was built
out from the ears in puffs, rolls,
and curls and often held in place
by wires as well as artificial hair.
These pompous topknots were
copied on dolls and could be

heart-shaped (the so-called
Venus knot fashioned in 20-05-
19) or a basketweave coil with a
well in the center (known as a
Beehive, as in 20-5-39).

The slender, sawdust-stuffed
body with its molded bosom,
small waist, and nonexistent
hips was an ideal vehicle for the
gowns of the period. The lady
doll on the right (20-5-39)—who
wears an original costume—is
clothed in a flowered dress
made of silk with long pantalets
showing beneath the hem of the
dress—all in very good taste,
but perhaps a style more appropriate to a young girl rather than
an adult. Although not visible in
the photograph, the doll on the
far left has an unusual swing-
jointed rather than unjointed kid
body.

Fig. 56
Lady
German
About 1830
According to museum records, "Purchased in France for New Orleans girl"
Papier-mâché shoulder head, molded painted black hair, painted features, unjointed kid body with carved wooden lower limbs, glued junction covered with paper bands, possibly original cotton dress, shirt, petticoat and pantalets
h 18"
20-05-16
Webb Collection, 1952-60

Lady
Germany
About 1830
Papier-mâché shoulder head, molded painted black hair, painted features, unjointed kid body with carved wooden lower limbs, glued junction covered with orange paper bands, original cotton organdy and lace dress
h 18"
20-05-17
Webb Collection, 1952-60

Lady
Germany
About 1830
Papier-mâché shoulder head, molded painted black hair, painted features, unjointed kid body with carved wooden lower limbs, glued junction covered with leather patches (repair), girl's cotton dress
h 12 1/2"
20-05-15
Webb Collection, 1952-60

Lady
Germany
About 1830
Papier-mâché shoulder head, molded painted black hair, painted features, unjointed kid body with carved wooden lower limbs, glued junction covered with paper bands, satin dress with silk shawl and handbag and metal brooch with colored stones
h 26 1/2"
20-05-61
Webb Collection, 1952-60

Lady
Germany
About 1830
Papier-mâché shoulder head, molded painted black hair, painted features, unjointed kid body with carved wooden lower limbs, glued junction covered with red kid bands, redressed in a girl's cotton dress and apron with cotton pantalets and petticoat by Marta Mengis in 1961
h 11 3/4"
20-05-90
Museum Purchase, 1961-104.2

These papier-mâché ladies with extravagant "dos" are sometimes called Adelaides. They are named after the German-born Princess Adelaide, the wife of William IV—Elector of Hanover and King of Great Britain—who was thought to be a highly fashion-conscious lady. During her husband's reign (1830-37) the enormous height and breadth of her hairstyles were renowned. The original costumes on the two dolls on the left confirm that the earlier high empire waistlines (see #20-11-113, fig. 29) had by this time moved down to a position where they remained until about 1900.

Fig. 57
Lady
Germany
About 1835
Papier-mâché shoulder head, molded painted black
hair ("Victoria" hairstyle), painted features, unjointed
cloth body with kid lower arms, kid hands with separate fingers, new cotton dress made in 2000 to copy
existing dress, pot metal necklace and brooch with
amber-colored stones
h 27"
20-05-79
Webb Collection, 1952-60

Lady
Germany
About 1835
Papier-mâché shoulder head, molded painted black
hair ("Victoria" hairstyle), brown glass eyes with painted upper and lower lashes, feathered brows and
deeply molded nostrils, cloth swing-jointed body with
leather hands, cotton dress
h 29"
20-05-80
Webb Collection, 1952-60

Fig. 58
Queen Victoria
Portrait on china exhibited at the Crystal Palace
Exposition in 1851 by Sèvres factory, France
Courtesy Eleanor St. George, *Dolls of Yesterday*

Queen Victoria provided a fashionable model for
many women beginning with her coronation on June
21, 1837. The center-parted hair is now braided at the
sides in long coils looped around or in front of the
ears to expose them and coiled into a bun in back. A
bust of Queen Victoria in the National Portrait Gallery
in London shows her hair dressed in this style.

Fig. 59
Lady
Germany
about 1835
papier-mâché shoulder
head, molded painted
black hair ("Victoria"
hairstyle), fine brush
strokes around face,
painted blue eyes,
unjointed kid body with
carved wooden lower
limbs, glued junction
covered with orange
paper bands, silk dress
17 3/4"
80-05-44
Webb Collection, 1952-60

Fig. 60
Lady
Germany
About 1840
Papier-mâché shoulder head,
molded painted black hair, painted features, unjointed kid body
with carved wooden lower limbs,
glued junction covered with
black paper bands, cotton pantalets, slip, and chemise
h 29"
20-05-35
Webb Collection, 1952-60

Twin Ladies
Germany
About 1840
Papier-mâché shoulder heads,
molded painted black hair, painted features, unjointed leather
bodies with carved wooden
lower limbs, glued junction covered with pink paper bands,
girl's cotton and silk dresses
h 11 1/2"
20-05-13a & b
Webb Collection, 1952-60

Lady
Germany
About 1840
Papier-mâché shoulder head,
molded painted black hair, painted features, unjointed kid body
with carved lower limbs, cotton
dress
h 13 3/4"
20-05-08
Webb Collection, 1952-60

Lady
Germany
About 1840
Papier-mâché shoulder head,
molded painted black hair, pain-
ed features, unjointed kid body
with carved wooden limbs
glued junction covered with
paper bands, silk dress with
bustle
h 16 3/4"
20-05-34
Webb Collection, 1952-60

Women's hairstyles in the 1840s, seen here on dolls of the period, became flat on top with a center
parting while the high knot gradually slipped from the top to the back of the head and down to the base
of the neck to become a flat wound hair knot called a chignon. The distinguished lady on the left is
unusually tall compared to her companions.

Fig. 61
Lady
Germany
About 1840
Papier-mâché shoulder head with molded chest plate,
molded painted black hair, painted features, unjointed
kid body with carved wooden lower limbs, glued junction covered with blue paper bands, cotton dress
h 18"
20-05-28
Webb Collection, 1952-60

Lady
Germany
About 1840
Papier-mâché shoulder head, molded painted black
hair, painted features, unjointed kid body with carved
wooden lower limbs, glued junction covered with
leather repair, original cotton dress
h 17 1/4"
20-05-12
Webb Collection, 1952-60

Lady
Germany
About 1840
Papier-mâché shoulder head with molded chest plate,
molded painted black hair, painted features, unjointed
kid body with carved wooden lower limbs, glued junction covered with blue paper bands, tarlatan net dress
h 21 1/2"
20-05-126
Gift of Miss Ruth Catlin, 1966-52.3

Period books and journals about women's hairstyles stress that "the principle in the arrangement of the hair around the forehead should be to preserve or assist the oval form of the face. As this differs in different individuals, the treatment should be adapted accordingly. The arrangement of the long hair at the base of the head is a matter of taste."[4] All three of these ladies have smoothly drawn center-parted hair waved behind the ears in long cascading curls hanging around the neck, which succeeds in accentuating the shape of their faces.

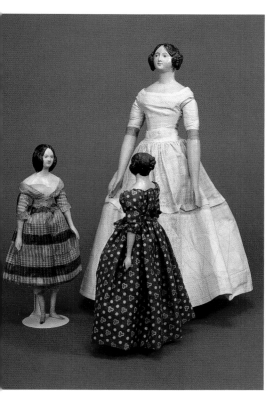

Fig. 62
Lady
Germany
About 1840
Papier-mâché shoulder head, molded painted black hair, painted features, unjointed kid body with carved wooden lower limbs, glued junction covered with paper bands, original silk dress
h 11 1/2"
20-05-09
Webb Collection, 1952-60

Lady
Germany
About 1840
Papier-mâché shoulder head, molded painted black hair, painted features, unjointed kid body with carved wooden lower limbs, glued junction covered with blue paper bands, old wool dress
h 11 1/2"
20-05-11
Webb Collection, 1952-60

Lady
Germany
About 1840
Papier-mâché shoulder head, molded painted black hair, painted features, unjointed kid body with carved wooden lower limbs, glued junction covered with red paper bands, original cotton underclothing
h 19 1/2"
20-05-97
Chandler Collection, 1962-262.15

The shared features of this 1840s hairstyle include a center part with curls over each ear pulled into a braided bun in the back. Particularly noteworthy is the original silk dress sewn onto the lady on the left and the tall doll's highly starched undergarments, consisting of featherstitched chemise and tucked petticoat with decorative diamond-shaped stitching.

Fig. 63
Lady
Germany
About 1840
Papier-mâché shoulder head, molded painted black hair, painted features, unjointed kid
body with carved wooden lower limbs, glued
junction covered with blue paper bands, old
wool paisley gown and cotton chemise, pantalets, and petticoat
h 22 1/8"
20-05-36
Webb Collection, 1952-60

Lady
Germany
About 1840
Papier-mâché shoulder head, molded painted black hair, painted features, unjointed kid
body with carved wooden lower arms, glued
junction covered with orange paper bands,
silk and flocked velvet dress
h 11 3/4"
20-05-42
Webb Collection, 1952-60

Lady
Germany
About 1840
Papier-mâché shoulder head, molded painted black hair, brown glass eyes, manufactured cloth swing-jointed body, old cotton
dress
h 27"
20-05-57
Webb Collection, 1952-60

Lady
Germany
About 1840
Papier-mâché shoulder head, molded painted
black hair, painted facial features, unjointed
kid body with carved wooden lower limbs,
glued junction covered with blue paper
bands, original girl's organdy dress and cotton pantalets, chemise, and petticoat
h 13 1/2"
20-05-21
Webb Collection, 1952-60

Lady
Germany
About 1840
Papier-mâché shoulder head, molded painted black hair, painted features, unjointed kid
body with carved wooden lower limbs
attached with red kidskin, old cotton print
dress, chemise, pantalets, and petticoat
h 24 1/2"
20-05-85
Webb Collection, 1952-60

Viewed from the front, side, and rear, all of
the ladies model an unusual hairstyle of the
1840s. This coiffure—known as oreilles du
chien—consists of hair parted in the center
and pulled down to the ears in a cluster of
shoulder-length sausage curls resembling
dogs' ears, then swept up into a braided bun
in the center of the back of the head.

Girl
Germany
About 1850
Papier-maché shoulder head, molded painted black hair, painted features, unjointed kid
body with carved wooden lower limbs, glued
junction covered with paper bands, original
cotton dress with bobbin lace at elbows and
collar, original cotton pantalets and petticoat
h 7"
20-05-114
Webb Collection, 1952-60

All three clothed dolls are sewn into their
original costumes. The undressed lady has
the expected side-by-side front-stitched body,
but it is made of cloth rather than kid, which
is unusual. This body is combined with the
typical carved lower limbs attached with
paper bands. These dolls also exhibit variations on the so-called "covered wagon" coiffure, with center-parted hair pulled smoothly
over the ears into vertical curls around the
head, a style most often found on China
dolls (See fig. 103, 20-02-69, 20 and 30).

Fig. 65
Girl
Germany
About 1850
Papier-maché shoulder head, molded painted black hair,
pupilless dark gray/brown glass eyes with painted upper and
lower lashes, feathered brows, cloth swing-jointed body with
leather arms, old taffeta dress and red boots
h 32 1/4"
20-05-73
Webb Collection, 1952-60

In addition to the lady dolls, which dominated the market
until about midcentury, children began to appear with distinctive round faces, short necks, and center-parted hair
pulled over the ears into short sausage curls around the
head, called a "covered wagon" coiffure on china dolls (see
fig. 103, dolls #20-02-69, 20 and 30). In addition, detailed
facial features include fixed glass eyes, feathered eyebrows,
and a pointed nose with deeply molded nostrils and red dots
inside. The doll is further distinguished by her sewn-on red
leather gloves and matching removable leather boots.

Fig. 66
Girl
Germany
About 1860
Papier-mâché shoulder head, molded painted black hair with center part pulled back
over ears with sausage curls around head,
pupilless brown glass eyes, painted upper
and lower lashes, cloth body swing-jointed
at shoulders, hips, and knees with lower kid
arms, cotton dress, apron, kid shoes
h 29 1/2"
20-05-53
Webb Collection, 1952-60

Girl
Germany
About 1860
Papier-mâché shoulder head, molded painted black hair with center part pulled back
behind ears with long sausage curls, pupilless brown glass flirty eyes, unjointed cloth
body with lower wooden limbs, original velvet and silk dress with lace Bertha sewed
onto body
h 24"
20-05-41
Webb Collection, 1952-60

Girl
Germany
About 1860
Papier-mâché shoulder head, molded painted black hair with center part pulled back
over ears with sausage curls around head,
painted features, wooden mortise-and-tenon
homemade body with upper leg portion
above knee joint missing
h 15"
20-05-26
Webb Collection, 1952-60

Lady
Germany
About 1860
Papier-mâché shoulder head, molded painted black hair with center part pulled back
over partially exposed ears with sausage
curls in back, painted features, unjointed kid
body with wooden lower limbs and painted
shoes, original silk and lace dress, cotton
pantalets, petticoat
h 16"
20-05-93
Chandler Collection, 1962-262.11

From 1850 to 1860 many firms in Germany
and America created play dolls that portray
an astounding variety in facial expression,
method of construction, and size. Both fixed
glass eyes (on 20-05-53) and even the flirty
eyes (on 20-05-41), invented in 1831 by E.
Pfranger from Hildburghausen, Germany,
which move side to side depending on the
position in which the doll is held, are
uncommon.[5] Painted eyes are still found
most frequently, as on the rest of these
dolls.

Fig. 67

Lady
Germany
About 1850
Papier-mâché shoulder head, molded painted black hair with center part and short curls
around face pulled back over partially
exposed ears into long curls down back with
shorter curls at nape, painted features with
nostril holes (breather), homemade cloth
swing-jointed body, old print dress, leather
shoes
h 32"
20-05-51
Webb Collection, 1952-60

Lady
Germany
About 1850
Papier-mâché shoulder head, molded painted black hair with center part pulled back
over exposed ears into long sausage curls
down back of neck, painted features, homemade cloth swing-jointed body stuffed with
cotton seed, original cotton dress
h 23"
20-05-92b
Chandler Collection, 1962-262.9

Girl
Germany
About 1850
Papier-mâché shoulder head, molded painted black hair with center part with wave at
sides pulled back into sausage curls around
head ("covered wagon" style), painted features, unjointed kid body with wooden lower
limbs attached with paper bands, old silk
jacket, cotton skirt
h 10 1/2"
20-05-23
Museum Collection, 2004-7

Lady
Germany
About 1850
Papier-mâché shoulder head, molded painted hair with center part swooped down in
front of exposed ears to mass of curls hanging down side of neck with back hair pulled
into braided bun at center of head, painted
features, unjointed leather body with carved
wooden limbs, old net dress
h 13"
20-05-10
Webb Collection, 1952-60

Lady
Germany
About 1850
Papier-mâché shoulder head, molded painted black hair with center part pulled back
around exposed ears into sausage curls in
back ("Greiner" style), pupilless brown glass
eyes, manufactured cloth swing-jointed
body, old cotton dress and underwear
including corset, red leather boots
h 35"
20-05-88
Museum Purchase, 1959-221.1

Because dolls were generally exported as
"heads only," the variety of bodies seen on
these two pages range from commercially
made unjointed kid (20-05-23) and manufactured cloth swing-jointed (20-05-88) styles
to homemade wooden (2-05-26) and cloth
(20-05-51) examples.

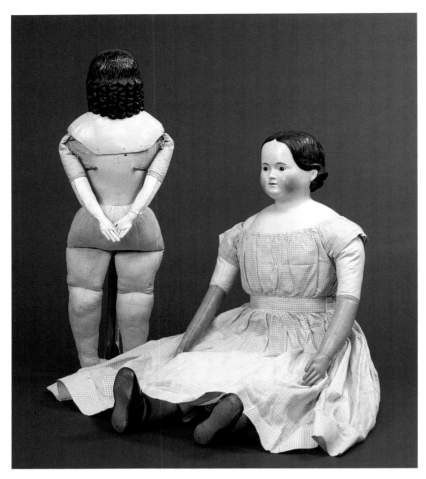

Fig. 68
Lady
German
About 1850
Papier-mâché shoulder head, molded painted black hair with center part pulled down to ears with long sausage curls on shoulders, painted features, manufactured cotton swing-jointed body with leather lower arms
h 25 ¹/₂"
20-05-58
Webb Collection, 1952-60

Lady
German
About 1850
Papier-mâché shoulder head, molded painted black hair with center part swept back over exposed ears with overall small curls in back, brown glass eyes, feathered eyebrows, highly colored cheeks, manufactured cotton swing-jointed body with lower leather arms, old cotton dress
h 33 ¹/₂"
Gift of the Van Stade Family, 1982-4.592

Both of these ladies have machine-stitched, manufactured swing-jointed cotton bodies with kid lower arms and individually stitched fingers. The doll on the left is distinguished by the bands with lace inserts that encircle the arm at the interface between upper and lower sections, the stitching at the waist which helps to define her posterior, and the detailed molding in her sausage finger curls.

Fig. 69
Child
Germany
About 1850
Papier-mâché shoulder head, molded painted black hair, painted features, unjointed kid body with carved wooden lower limbs, glued junction covered with blue paper bands, wool dress, cotton pantalets, petticoat
h 8 ³/₄"
20-05-25
Webb Collection, 1952-60

Child
Germany
About 1850
Papier-mâché shoulder head, molded painted black hair, painted features, unjointed kid body with carved wooden lower limbs, glued junction covered with blue paper bands, original silk damask blouse, silk satin skirt, cotton pantalets, and petticoat sewn onto body
h 8 ¹/₂"
20-05-24
Webb Collection, 1952-60

These twin girls with short, all-over curls have fine painted features with delicate brush strokes around the face as well as brown eyes with pupils. Furthermore, the doll at right is dressed in her original clothing, consisting of a silk satin skirt fabricated from a wide ribbon.

Fig. 70
Boy
Germany
About 1850
Papier-mâché shoulder head, molded painted black hair, painted features, unjointed kid body with carved wooden lower limbs, original silk trousers and wool jacket sewn onto body
h 17 3/4"
20-05-31
Webb Collection, 1952-60

Boy
Germany
About 1850
Papier-mâché shoulder head, molded painted black hair, painted features, handmade unjointed cloth body, homemade plaid pants and vest
h 23"
20-05-92a
Chandler Collection, 1962-262.10

Fewer male dolls were made than either ladies or girls. Like their adult counterparts, these boys wear medium-length hair combed towards the face, which in both cases is delineated by fine brushstrokes around the forehead.

Fig. 71
Lady and Gentleman
Probably Germany
About 1850
Papier-mâché shoulder head, molded painted black curly hair, brown painted eyes with black pupils, red dots in corners and in nostrils, unjointed cloth body except at shoulders, carved wooden arms and legs, original clothing
h 12 1/2"
20-05-107, 108
Webb Collection, 1952-60

It rare to find African American papier-mâché dolls, especially those that survive in their original costumes. This lady wears a printed wool dress with organdy undersleeves, trimmed with bracelets at each cuff made of brown beads, and cotton pantalets with petticoat. The most unusual feature is her remarkable silk bonnet with a curly spun wool "wig" glued around the front, framing her face. The gentleman is dressed in a dashing outfit consisting of silk pants, a velvet jacket lined with striped silk ribbons, and a matching silk vest with steel bead buttons, a linen shirt with collar, and a silk cravat.

Fig. 72
Lady
Hildburghausen, Germany
Attributed to Andreas Voit
About 1850
Papier-mâché shoulder head, molded
painted black hair, pupilless brown glass
eyes with painted upper and lower lashes, feathered eyebrows, deeply molded
nostrils, cloth swing-jointed body with
percale arms and stitched fingers, cotton dress, petticoat, and pantalets, gold-
colored glass bead necklace
h 29"
20-05-65
Webb Collection, 1952-60

Girl
Hildburghausen, Germany
Attributed to Andreas Voit
About 1850
Papier-mâché shoulder head, molded
painted black hair, pupilless brown glass
eyes with painted upper and lower lashes, manufactured cloth swing-jointed
body with lower kid hands, stitched
toes, old cotton dress, pantalets, petticoat, and chemise, gold-colored glass
beaded necklace added later
h 23"
20-05-40
Webb Collection, 1952-60

The shape of the face and size of the neck distinguish the adult from the child.
However, both have short molded hair with wispy brushstrokes around the forehead, painted eyelashes, and fixed glass eyes. The barefoot young lady on the right
shows off her professionally made cloth body with individually stitched toes.

Both of these dolls probably originated at the distinguished factory of Andreas Voit
in Hildburghausen. Although he never marked his dolls, some surviving examples
in the Hildburghausen museum have a documented history or provenance and
can be compared to unidentified models such as these. Voit papier-mâché dolls
often have glass eyes and detailed painting of hairstyle and eyelashes like these.
For example, the coiffure on the taller lady is molded and painted exactly like one
given to the town museum by a former employee of the Voit company in 1900.[6]

Fig. 73
Lady
Hildburghausen, Germany
Head attributed to Andreas Voit; body
France
1820-70
h 32 1/2"
Papier-mâché shoulder head, nailed-on
brown human hair wig, pupilless brown
glass eyes, painted features, cloth
swing-jointed body with lower leather
arms, old cotton dress
h 32 1/2"
20-05-77
Webb Collection, 1952-60

Gentleman
Hildburghausen, Germany
Head attributed to Andreas Voit; body
France
1820-70
Papier-mâché shoulder head, nailed-on
brown human hair wig, pupilless brown
glass eyes, painted features, unjointed
kid French-type body, swing-jointed
leather arms, velvet suit
h 31 3/4"
20-05-69
Webb Collection, 1952-60

Some of the dolls attributed to Andreas Voit are erroneously called "French Papier
Mâché." Although the heads were manufactured at Voit's Hildburghausen,
Germany, factory, they were sent to Paris and given fashionable hairstyles with
nailed-on human hair wigs. These were then attached to typical French unjointed
kid bodies that were pink in color and tightly stuffed. The completed dolls were
dressed in the newest fashions and sold throughout the world as what the market
called "Paris dolls." Chief buyers were, in addition to the French and English, the
Americans.[7]

Fig. 74
Lady
Hildburghausen, Germany
Possibly Andreas Voit
About 1840
Papier-mâché shoulder
head, molded painted hair
under brown human-hair
wig, pupilless brown glass
eyes, open mouth with
four articulated bamboo
teeth, cloth swing-jointed
body with leather arms
(body not original to
head), cotton chemise,
petticoat, pantalets, stockings
h 30"
20-05-86
Museum Purchase

Lady
Hildburghausen, Germany
Possibly Andreas Voit
About 1850
Papier-mâché shoulder
head, painted brush
stroke black hair (should
have human-hair wig),
pupilless brown glass
eyes, open mouth with
square bamboo teeth (breather), manufactured gusseted French (pink-dyed) kid body with large posteri-
or, cotton dress, pantalets, petticoat sewn onto body
h 21"
20-05-70
Webb Collection, 1952-60

After 1840, manufacturer's catalogue pages of the Andreas Voit company show doll heads with open mouths with set-in upper or lower rows of teeth made of bamboo.[8] The lady on the right has a painted black spot with brush marks to suggest stray hairs. However, holes surrounding the pate indicate a wig had been applied to the head in the past.

Fig. 75
Lady
Germany
About 1870
Papier-mâché shoulder head, molded painted blonde hair, painted features, cloth
swing-jointed body with leather lower arms
(body not original to doll), cotton dress,
socks, pantalets, chemise, and petticoat
h 34"
20-05-76
Webb Collection, 1952-60

This lady of about 1870 has an unusual
hairstyle with molded blonde hair pulled
away from the face and held in back with a
long comb above soft curls. She has deeply
molded nostrils and is also referred to by
collectors as a "breather" because of the
open holes in her nose, although there is
no actual internal respiratory mechanism.
Her elaborate cotton petticoat is stitched in
tiers with eyelet and tatted lace.

Fig. 76
Lady
Philadelphia, Pennsylvania, United States
Ludwig Greiner
1858
Printed paper label on back of shoulder plate: Greiner's/patent
Heads/No 12/Pat. March 30th '58"
Stamped in black ink on lower back of torso: 12 (head size)
Written in brown ink on back of lower torso: nsd/nde [possibly pricing
or inventory marks]
Papier-mâché shoulder head, molded painted black hair, painted
features with two ring blue eyes, manufactured cloth swing-jointed
body with lower leather arms, cotton dress, chemise, pantalets,
petticoat, blue kid shoes
h 31 ¹/₂"
20-05-74
Webb Collection, 1952-60

Lady
Philadelphia, Pennsylvania, United States
Philip Lerch
About 1858-79
Printed paper label on back of shoulder: Lerch and Co.,
Manufacturers
Papier-mâché shoulder head, molded painted black hair, painted
features, manufactured cloth swing-jointed body with leather lower
arms, old cotton dress and underwear, leather shoes
h 32 ¹/₂"
20-05-66
Webb Collection, 1952-60

Girl
Philadelphia, Pennsylvania, United States
Ludwig Greiner
1872
Printed paper label on back of shoulder plate: Greiner's Patent doll
Heads #4 Pat. March 30, 58 ext 72"
Papier-mâché shoulder head, molded painted blonde hair, painted
features, cloth swing-jointed body with lower kid arms, cotton pan-
talets, striped stockings, leather boots
h 21"
20-05-45
Webb Collection, 1952-60

The first American doll patent was issued to Ludwig Greiner in 1858
for improving the cloth reinforcement in the head seams as well as
linen or muslin wadded reinforcement to protect projecting chins
and noses. An extension of the patent was granted in 1872. Ranging
in size from thirteen inches (size 0) to thirty-five inches (size 13),
most Greiner heads have black hair with a center part, exposed ears
and sausage curls, while later models had blonde hair in a shorter,
windblown style. The rare tall, deep shoulder head bearing a Philip
Lerch label has distinctively modeled hair with three waves on either
side of the face originating from a high center part and ending in
back just above the nape of the rather thick neck. She and the
labeled Lerch lady at the Strong Museum (79.512) share delicate features, including painted blue eyes with a large central black pupil
and a somewhat surprised expression.

Fig. 77
Lady
Sonneberg, Germany
Müller & Strasburger
about 1880
Printed paper label on back of shoulder
plate: M & S/Superior/ 2015
Papier-mâché shoulder head, molded painted blonde hair, painted features, manufactured cloth swing-jointed body, leather
hands, possibly original cotton dress, chemise, pantalets, eyelet petticoat and tucked
petticoat
h 37"
20-05-49
Webb Collection, 1952-60

Lady
Sonneberg, Germany
Müller & Strasburger
about 1880
Printed paper label on back of shoulder
plate: M & S/Superior/2015
Papier-mâché shoulder head, molded painted blonde hair, painted features, cloth
swing-jointed body with kid lower arms, old
cotton petticoat
h 35"
20-05-89
Museum Purchase, 1959-221.1

Girl
Sonneberg, Germany
Müller & Strasburger
1880-90
Printed paper label on back of shoulder
plate: M & S/Superior/2015
Early composition shoulder head, molded
painted black hair, painted features, homemade cloth body jointed only at hips, old
cotton print dress and apron
h 32 1/2"
20-05-67
Webb Collection, 1952-60

The Sonneberg firm of Müller and
Strasburger was in business from about
1844 to 1892. Both blonde and brunette
models with the M & S label have been
found on either manufactured or homemade
cloth bodies. These examples have deep
shoulder plates, sloping shoulders and distinctive three-color eyes consisting of a blue
pupil surrounded by outer rings of slate gray
and dark blue with highlights.

Fig. 78
Girl
Sonneburg, Germany
Cuno and Otto Dressel
About 1880
Stamped on rear shoulder plate: "HOLZ-MASSE"
Composition shoulder head, molded painted blonde hair, painted features, cotton
swing- jointed body with leather arms, old blue wool dress and sewn-on striped
socks
h 20"
20-05-46
Webb Collection, 1952-60

In 1875, Cuno and Otto Dressel registered one of the first known German doll
trademarks with the newly formed patent office in Sonneberg. Their design consisted of a winged scepter and helmet over an oval containing the word "HOLZ-
MASSE," which appears stamped on the rear shoulder plate. These German words
for wood-pulp composition indicates a mixture of various ingredients designed to
be "indestructible"—a rather optimistic claim. In 1876 the company displayed lady
dolls at the Philadelphia Exposition and were "commended for great variety, solid
material and cheapness, especially heads with good-looking features."[9] This well-
painted head has blue eyes with black eyeliner, fringed lower lashes, feathered
brows, nostrils accented with red circle dots, and closed lips with a centerline.

Wax Dolls

The virtues of wax as a modeling material have been evident for centuries. Wax has been used to create religious effigies, funerary figures, and jewelry. Its superb versatility led to its practical application in the creation of detailed wax models for teaching medicine in England in the eighteenth century. Madame Tussaud, a friend of King Louis XVI's sister, excelled in this medium before she fled the French Revolution and arrived in England in 1802. She brought with her a collection of death masks of guillotined aristocrats. Her successful wax works show traveled all over the British Isles and finally settled permanently in London. The art of wax portraiture drew many skilled foreign artists and craftsmen to London to seek employment in the field and it is likely that, responding to the growing demand for playthings of all kinds, some of them made dolls. Wax doll making flourished from 1850 to 1900 due largely to the work of Italian immigrants to England such as the Pierotti and Montanari families. Impetus to the industry can also be attributed to the influence of the young Queen Victoria, who prompted these talented foreign-born craftsmen to depict the faces of her nine royal children in miniature wax form.[1]

Translucent, luminous, and warm to the touch, wax can faithfully reproduce human facial features and skin tones. Three major types of material were used—beeswax, with its warm color, and spermaceti and paraffin wax, which are harder

continued on next page

Fig. 79
Girl
London, England
Probably John Edwards
about 1875
Poured-wax shoulder head, inserted blonde human hair on head, eyebrows, and eyelashes, blue glass sleep eyes, cloth swing-jointed body with poured arms and legs, embroidered cotton dress with silk bow
23"
0-10-41
Chandler Collection, 1962-262.31

John Edwards was one of the few doll artists who actually mass-produced poured-wax dolls in his six-floor factory, established in 1868. Nearly twenty thousand wax dolls were reportedly completed there each week and wholesaled to London toy shops during the Victorian era. According to Edwards's advertisements, he made dolls copied from well-known paintings, and the range of the company's products included "young lady dolls of large size, attired in morning, dinner or ball costumes, there are baby dolls, most elaborately dressed in muslin and lace, character dolls such as Mother Hubbard and Little Red Riding Hood, Highlanders . . . mechanical dolls which move their heads and imitate breathing by means of clockwork . . . fancy models for displaying the wares of the milliner."[2]

Apparently, they were exquisitely modeled just like this young girl, with articulated and molded fingernails and toes, implanted hair, eyelashes, and eyebrows as well as weighted sleep eyes. In 1854 the doll factory of C. F. Maier, Nürnberg, presented sleeping eyes that operate on the following principle: when the lead weight, attached to the eyeballs by a short wire is down—parallel to the face—the eyes remain open. When the doll is placed in a horizontal position and the weight drops back into the head—at right angles to the face—the eyes close.[3]

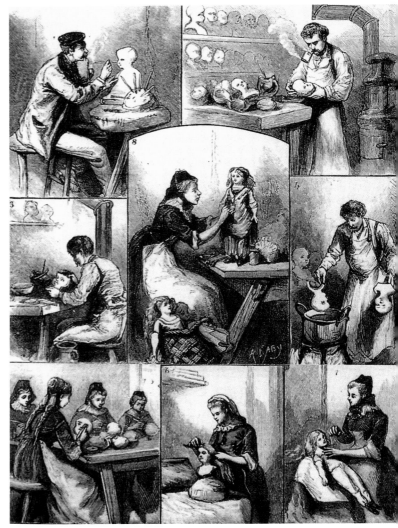

and whiter. However, it is difficult to determine which has been used without taking a sample—or more recently, examination using such procedures as ultraviolet light, gas chromatography, or infrared spectroscopy. Wax dolls were produced in two different ways and can thus be considered in two separate categories. The nineteenth-century English firms were most famous for their poured wax. In the first stage in this manufacturing process, an artist who created the pattern modeled the head in wax or clay. From this, a cast was produced in the form of a two- or three-part plaster mold. The mixture of molten wax and coloring was poured into this negative space and allowed to set for a brief time before the excess mixture was poured out. This process could be repeated several more times to create a number of layers, resulting in a final thickness of no more than an eighth of an inch. The more layers of wax and color, the more lifelike the appearance of the doll and the more durable the head. Once cooled and solidified, the finished casting was separated from the mold and skillfully finished. The eyeholes were cut, the blown glass eyes set into the socket, and the human hair or mohair applied. Finally, the cheeks, nostrils, and lips were painted. Poured-wax heads usually had deep shoulder plates—a one-piece casting made of wax and consisting of head, neck, upper shoulders, and front and back chest plates. This complete unit was sewn to the cloth body stuffed with animal hair or sawdust through holes strategically placed at the bottom corners of the front and back plates. Most poured-wax arms and legs were cast to above the elbow and knee joints. They often had metal grommets embedded in wax holes which were attached to the upper stuffed cloth limbs, in the same way as the head was joined to the torso.

Wax-over-papier-mâché dolls were first developed by Heinrich Stier of Sonneberg, Germany in 1852 and are decidedly different in construction from their English counterparts.[4] They were also significantly cheaper both to manufacture and buy as well as more durable than their poured-wax relatives. Papier-mâché firms simply used their regular production models under an overcoat of wax in an effort to produce a more naturalistic appearance. However, these dolls more commonly appeared as a complete unit, being sold by the manufacturer attached to the commercial body. An engraving in an 1887 issue of *The Queen, The Lady's Newspaper* illustrates the eight steps in the process of German wax doll manufacture—making the model, joining the head, setting the eyes, waxing the head, painting the face, dressing the hair, fixing the head, and dressing the finished doll (fig. 80).

The Shelburne Museum collection encompasses both English and German poured and wax-overs (as well as two-faced and hatted examples), including dolls attributed to John Edwards, Mme. Augusta Montanari, Mrs. Lucy Peck, and the only known example signed by Anthony Bazzoni, all working in London.

Fig. 81
Girls called "Plymouth Belles"
England
1801
Wax-over-papier-mâché shoulder head, glued-on brown human hair, brown glass eyes, unjointed cloth bodies with dyed lower leather arms and separate fingers, original tarlatan clothing, straw hats
16, 20, 15"
20-10-26, 20-10-28, 20-10-27
Museum Purchase, 1959-14.1-3

These dolls are remarkable for their well-documented history. According to the past owner, Miss Mary Jackson of Plymouth, Massachusetts, who was in her eighties, her great-grandfather brought the dolls home as a gift to his three children in 1801. Shortly thereafter a mahogany and glass silk-lined case was made and the dolls hung in the ancestral house for many years. They were known as the Plymouth Belles, the handsomest dolls in town. Aside from their provenance, the dolls are sewn into their original high-waist, empire-style dresses, decorated with silver braid, tassels, and sequins.

Fig. 82
Girl
London, England
Probably John Edwards
About 1875
Poured-wax shoulder head, inserted blonde human hair on head, eyebrows, and eyelashes, blue glass sleep eyes, cloth swing-jointed body with poured arms and legs, embroidered cotton dress with silk bow
h 23"
20-10-41
Chandler Collection, 1962-262.31

Girl
England
Probably Augusta Montanari
1850-60
Poured-wax shoulder head, individually rooted brown human hair, blue threaded-glass eyes, cloth swing-jointed body with lower wax arms and legs attached through grommets, cotton and lace clothing, kid shoes
h 27 1/2"
20-10-22
Webb Collection, 1952-1960

The Great Exhibition of 1851, held at the Crystal Palace in London, helped to establish the reputations of many doll makers. One of these was Madame Augusta Montanari, who won her first medal at this event. The judges singled out her creations as the "most remarkable and beautiful collection of Toys in the Great Exhibition. It is a series of dolls representing all ages, from infancy to womanhood . . . the dolls have hair, eyelashes, and eyelids separately inserted in wax . . . a variety of expressions are given to the figures in regard to the ages and stations which they are intended to represent. The dolls are adapted for children of the wealthy rather than general sale."[5]

Aside from the seated girl's meticulously rooted and parted hair, other realistic details include tinted (originally pink, now faded) limbs, articulated fingers and even molded fingernails and toes. All of these artistic features suggest that Madame Montanari and her family created her.

Fig. 83
Girl
England
About 1880
Wax-over-papier-mâché shoulder head, glued and nailed blonde mohair wig with black skull cap, brown glass sleep eyes, painted features, new cotton swing-jointed body with kid arms and triangle-stitched foot with five stitched fingers and toes.
h 25"
20-10-51
Gift of Mrs. Mary Best, 1985-11.1

Girl
London, England
About 1898
Mrs. Lucy Peck
Stamped rectangle on stomach: from Mrs. Peck the doll's home 131 Regent Street W
Poured-wax shoulder head, blond inserted human hair, blue threaded-glass paperweight eyes, painted features, cloth body with poured-wax lower limbs attached with metal grommets, gingham dress, leather shoes
h 27"
20-10-29
Gift of Miss Katharine Woodell, 1959-182

These two dolls, produced in England during the last quarter of the nineteenth century, show the range of materials and construction techniques used for heads (wax over papier-mâché as opposed to poured wax) hair, (mohair wig or human inserted), and eyes (brown glass sleep or blue glass stationary). The girl on the right is stamped by Lucy Peck, who is best known for her wax portrait doll of Queen Victoria, although she also made wax dolls depicting Victorian ladies in fashions of the day. At her store on Regent Street she sold many other items besides her own poured-wax dolls, which she produced until about 1911. Peck's doll at right is fitted with so-called threaded paperweight eyes, referring to blown glass with the irises having drawn white threads through them to give a depth of color and luminosity similar to that found in fine paperweights.

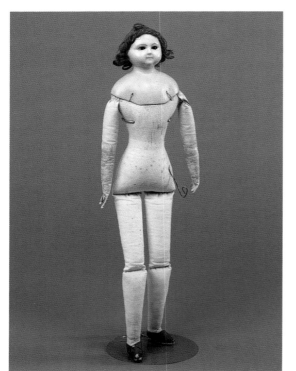

Fig. 84
Lady
Germany
About 1840
Wax-over-papier-mâché wire shoulder head, slit head with brown human hair wig, brown glass sleep eyes worked by a wire through the body, painted features, manu-factured cloth swing-jointed body, leather arms and shoes
h 17"
20-10-09
Webb Collection, 1952-60

Some wax-over papier-mâché dolls such as this one have slits down the center of the head for inserting tresses of hair. This lady is also fitted with an eye-wire mech-anism and pull loop protruding from the side of the body, invented by E. Pfränger of Hildburghausen, Germany, in 1831.[6] The external wire runs up through the body and is hooked to an interlocking circle formed from the wires connected to each glass eye. When the body wire is pulled down, the eyes open; when the body wire is pushed up, the eyes close. This method offers several advantages compared to weighted eyes: the doll can lie down without falling asleep and she can sleep when sitting up. This hand-operated mechanism provided one more way in which a little girl could manipulate the actions of her plaything.

Fig. 85
Girl
England
About 1830
Beeswax-over-papier-mâché shoulder head, blonde mohair wig cap, brown glass eyes, painted features, cloth swing-jointed body with lower leather arms, cotton and silk dress trimmed with metal ribbon and lace
h 15 1/2"
20-10-35
Chandler Collection, 1962-262.24

Lady
England
About 1810
Wax over carved wooden head and body, blonde human-hair wig with braid in back, brown glass eyes, cloth upper arms, wooden lower limbs (also waxed) attached at hips and knees by pegged mortise-and-tenon joints, original brocade gown with metal lace
h 20"
20-10-24
Webb Collection, 1952-60

Girl
England
About 1810
Poured-wax shoulder head, molded painted black hair, brown bead eyes, cloth swing-jointed body at hips, poured wax upper arms (hands missing), silk dress
h 11 1/2"
20-10-33
Chandler Collection, 1962-262.22

These early nineteenth-century wax dolls reveal the versatility of wax and its ability to be used both in a solid state or as a coating over other materials. Furthermore, x-rays reveal that the lady in the middle is unusual because she is constructed like an English wooden doll. While the head appears to be made of poured wax, it is actually wood covered in a thick coating of wax, as are all four limbs. Her long-sleeved bodice, which has never been removed, is original.

Fig. 86
Lady
Probably English
About 1880
Poured-wax shoulder head, glued-on brown mohair wig, brown glass bead eyes, painted features, cloth unjointed body with poured wax arms and wooden legs, original cotton dress, silk shawl, and reticule, straw bonnet edged with fabric flowers
h 9 1/2"
20-10-07
Webb Collection, 1952-60

Lady
Probably English
About 1890
Poured-wax shoulder head, glued-on brown mohair wig, painted features, cloth unjointed body with wax hands and wooden legs, original silk dress, silk bonnet, cotton apron, reed basket with chenille flower and strawberries
h 9 1/2"
20-10-08
Webb Collection, 1952-60

These two wax shoulder-head ladies are dressed in their original costumes complete with bonnet and basket accessories. The doll on the left is fitted with glass bead eyes set into the head.

Fig. 87
Bride
Germany
About 1872
Wax-over-papier-mâché shoulder head, blonde mohair wig, brown glass eyes, painted features, pierced ears with bead earrings, cloth swing-jointed body, wax-over papier-mâché arms, original satin wedding gown, cotton petticoat and pantalets
h 27"
20-10-46
Chandler Collection, 1962-262.132

According to Shelburne Museum accession records, this elegant lady was dressed for the "Friendship" Fair on December 7, 1872, in Lancaster, Pennsylvania, where she won a prize for her bridal outfit. She was purchased to raise money for the Sanitary Commission—the predecessor of the American Red Cross—which provided hospital relief for soldiers during the Civil War. She is exhibited with her original, elaborate cotton petticoat decorated with bands of vertical gathers and trimmed with a flounce of lace.

Fig. 88
Taufling Baby
Sonneberg, Germany
Louis Lindner & Söhne
About 1880
Beeswax-over-papier-mâché shoulder head, blonde mohair ringlets, brown glass sleep eyes, painted features, cloth upper body with turned wooden arms and legs with floating joints at wrists and ankles secured with string to composition feet and hands, bellows box in chest
h 22"
20-10-14
Webb Collection, 1952-60

Taufling Baby
Germany
About 1850
Wax-over-papier-mâché shoulder head, blue painted eyes and facial features, cloth body with papier-mâché arms, hands, hips, legs, and feet with floating string-joints at wrists and ankles
h 7 ¹/₂"
20-03-146
Webb Collection, 1952-60

At the 1851 London Crystal Palace Exhibition, the Japanese presented a doll with an unusual loose-limbed body like that of a young baby. Edmund Lindner, dollmaker of Sonneberg, was intrigued with the design and commissioned a similar doll to be made in his own country. Known as "Taufling" (from the German word *tauflinge* referring to babies before they are christened), various makers produced the doll for fifty years using different head materials, including wax, papier mâché, and porcelain. No matter which material was used, they all had a cloth body with wood or composition hands and feet attached directly to shoulders and hips respectively with string. This enabled the hands and feet to rotate freely or float. These dolls could have squeak "mama" crier bellows, glass or painted eyes, fabric wigs or painted hair, and either open or closed mouths.

ig. 89
irl
ermany
360-90
andwritten on tag: Mary Jane/made in
mous Augsburg Germany factory/in 1867.
rized possession/of a Richmond, KY
hild/Miss Molly Fifer/given to her in 1873
ax-over papier-mâché shoulder head,
onde mohair wig with braided coronet,
rown glass wire sleep eyes, painted fea-
res, ears pierced into head with earrings,
oth swing-jointed body with lower compo-
tion limbs, redressed in old tarlatan and
ce child's dress by Marta Mengis in 1962,
otton pantalets
26"
0-10-36
handler Collection, 1962-262.25

irl
ermany
bout 1850
ax-over-papier-mâché shoulder head,
rown mohair wig, brown glass eyes with
eep eye wire, manufactured cloth body
ith lower kid arms, embroidered dress,
ather shoes
13"
0-10-06
ebb Collection, 1952-60

Lady
Germany
About 1870
Wax-over-papier-mâché shoulder head,
blonde mohair wig in bun woven with flowers and lace, blue glass sleep eyes, ears
pierced into head with metal earrings, faux
pearl necklace, cloth swing-jointed body,
papier mâché lower arms and lower legs,
original organdy dress with ribbon trim, cotton petticoats and chemise, leather gloves
and boots
h 19 1/2"
20-10-53
Gift of Mr. Allen B. Harbach, 1991-11.2

Lady
Sonneberg, Germany
Probably made by Cuno and Otto Dressel
About 1870
Marked on shoulder plate in front: XXXI
Pencil marks on cloth body: JSL/XXX2X
Wax-over-papier-mâché shoulder head,
blonde mohair wig in loose ringlets, painted
features, beads embedded in neck, molded
corset on edge of shoulder plate, cloth swing-
jointed body, china lower arms and legs
(probably not original)
h 24 3/4"
20-10-34
Chandler Collection, 1962-262.23

These four wax-over papier-mâché shoulder
heads exhibit a variety of elaborate hairstyles. The "doll hairdressers" worked in
small workshops or in special departments
of doll factories to produce wigs either glued
directly on the closed doll head, stuck (20-
10-34) or sewed (20-10-36 and 20-10-6) onto
a gauze cap or inserted into a slit down the
center (20-10-09 See fig. 84).[7] X-rays reveal
that the wig on 20-10-53 is attached to a
hollow composition pate inserted into the
front of the head, which also allowed the
sleep-eye mechanism to be inserted.
Mohair, from the angora goat, was the pre-
ferred material because it is silkier and
smoother than human hair, but it was three
times as expensive. The undressed doll has
a remarkable molded blouse with applied
lace trim also found on several other dolls
marked by Cuno and Otto Dressel, the old-
est, largest, and most well-known manufacturer and exporter of toys and dolls in
Sonneberg, Germany.

Fig. 90
Girl
Germany
About 1880
Wax-over-papier-mâché shoulder head,
molded painted blonde hair, brown glass
sleep eyes, cloth swing-jointed body with
voice box, lower wooden arms and legs,
original cotton dress
h 13 ¹/₂"
20-10-54
Gift of Ms. Christine Wentworth, 1994-20

Girl
Germany
About 1880
Wax-over-papier-mâché shoulder head,
molded painted blonde hair, brown glass
bug eyes, new cloth body with composition
limbs
h 25 ¹/₂"
20-10-17
Webb Collection, 1952-60

Twin Girls
Germany
About 1860
Wax-over-papier-mâché shoulder heads,
molded blonde hair, brown glass eyes, cloth
swing-jointed body with papier-mâché arms
and wooden lower limbs, original cotton
dresses
h 13 ³/₄"
20-10-04a and b
Webb Collection, 1952-60

The most significant advance in the evolution of the wax-over-papier-mâché type of doll was
the so-called "pumpkin head" or "squash head" doll, dating from the mid-nineteenth century.
Their round, moon-like faces are very narrow from front to back and more closely represent
children than adults. This cheaper doll was produced from shallow, two- rather than three-
part molds so that drying could be accelerated and the danger of warping reduced.[8] Most
examples have blonde hair molded in an upswept style with a rather Germanic-looking roll
of hair at the back or rows of vertical curls. Often ribbons, bows, or combs were included
in the mold.

Fig. 91
Lady
Germany
About 1870
Wax-over-papier-mâché shoulder head, molded painted blonde hair
with large brimmed hat, brown glass eyes, kid swing-jointed body and
upper limbs, bulbous wax-over-composition lower arms and legs, old
cotton underclothes, newly made cotton chemise
H 23"
20-10-32
Chandler Collection, 1962-262.21

Lady
Probably Germany
About 1870
Wax-over-composition shoulder head with pierced ears, molded paint-
ed brown hair, molded top hat with ribbon, brown glass eyes, cloth
swing-jointed body with wooden arms and legs attached with paper
strips, silk dress
H 17 1/2"
20-10-45
Chandler Collection, 1962-262.37

Lady
Germany
About 1880
Wax-over-composition shoulder head, molded painted hat trimmed
with a feather, traces of mohair along back of head, brown glass eyes,
cloth swing-jointed body with internal squeak box, composition lower
arms, wooden legs, cotton and organdy dress with lace trim
H 21 1/4"
20-10-31
Gift of Mrs. Marshall E. Farnham, 1962-118.1

These three ladies, primarily made in Germany, illustrate the popularity as well as the variety of fashionable hats during the Victorian era.
The fancy bonnets on these dolls include a broad brim with a bow, a
tall hat with a long ribbon, and a Cossack-style cap with a feather.

Fig. 92
Boy
Germany
About 1870
Wax-over-composition shoulder head to waist with molded hat, brown
glass bug eyes, molded painted brown hair, painted features, cloth
swing-jointed body with lower composition arms and carved wooden
legs, old tarlatan pants, original cotton shirt and paper hat
H 15 1/3"
20-10-05
Webb Collection, 1952-60

During the period 1860-80 some wax doll variations included headgear. In this case, the doll's yellow boater is made of painted paper
with a black paper band. This hatted boy is an example of an inexpensive doll in his original costume made of tarlatan—a stiffened open-
weave muslin used for Christmas stockings. In addition, x-rays reveal
an internal spring inserted at the waist between two pieces of wood,
which probably once housed a bellows. This squeak-box mechanism
was operated by pushing the doll downwards.

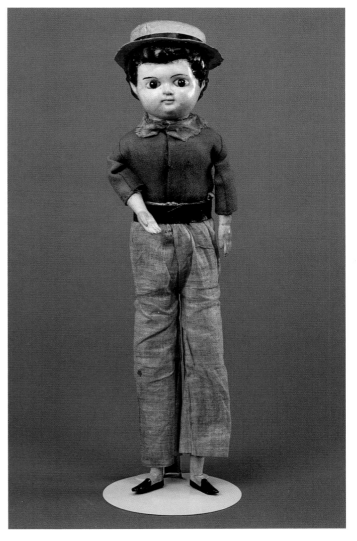

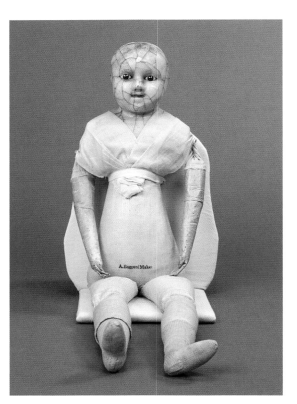

Fig. 93
Child
London, England
Anthony Bazzoni
About 1850
Stamped on front lower torso in black ink: A. Bazzoni Maker
Wax-over-papier-mâché shoulder head, brown threaded-glass eyes, open/closed mouth with four teeth, painted facial features, cloth swing-jointed body stuffed with sawdust with lower kid arms, brass-headed steel pins in crown of head to hold wig (now missing)
h 28 1/2"
20-10-20
Webb Collection, 1952-60

Affectionately known as "scary baby" to Shelburne Museum staff, this very rare and important doll is the only known marked example by Anthony Bazzoni, a London maker who invented the Speaking Doll with "papa" and "mamma"' internal bellows. An Italian craftsman, Bazzoni and his family emigrated to London in the early 1800s; there he started his doll making business. The most striking features of this baby are her blown glass eyes with spider web threads throughout the iris. Her face reveals the inherent problems of wax over papier-mâché, which is subject to crazing caused by the expansion and contraction of both materials occurring at different rates. Over time, black-colored grime has become embedded in the cracks. The conservation department is undertaking research to determine a nondestructive method for removing this residue. To date, no satisfactory solution has been discovered, and the Bazzoni baby is in storage awaiting treatment.

Fig. 94
Baby
Germany
About 1850
One-piece poured-wax head, body, and legs, glued-on blonde mohair wig, blue glass eyes, poured-wax arms jointed at shoulders, gauze dress
h 8"
20-10-16b
Webb Collection, 1952-60

Girl
Germany
About 1880
One-piece poured-wax head, body, and legs, blonde mohair wig, blue glass eyes, poured-wax arms joined at shoulders, cotton shift
h 7 1/4"
20-10-47
Webb Collection, 1952-60

Baby
Germany
About 1890
One-piece poured-wax head and body, no hair, molded painted features, poured-wax arms and legs jointed at shoulders and hips
h 4"
20-10-23
Gift of Miss Agnes Carlisle, 1953-97

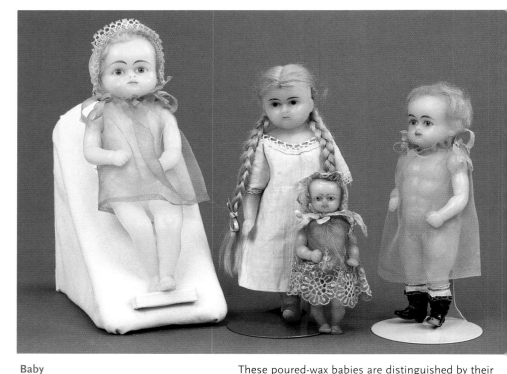

Baby
Germany
About 1850
One-piece poured-wax head, body, and legs, glued-on blonde mohair wig, blue glass eyes, poured-wax arms jointed at shoulders, gauze dress
h 8"
20-10-16a
Webb Collection, 1952-60

These poured-wax babies are distinguished by their one-piece construction for head, body, and legs as well as their small size: all of them are less than eight inches high. The twins on either end were actually modeled in a recumbent position with bent limbs and were sold either nude or in a shift.

Fig. 95
Two-Faced Doll
Sonneberg, Germany
Fritz Bartenstein
1880
Stamped on front of body: Deutshland
Written on body in pale ink: Schenhut
Wax-over-papier-mâché swivel head, papier-mâché
molded blouse shoulder plate, brown glass eyes,
painted features, cloth swing-jointed body, composition lower limbs on cardboard cylinder body housing
head turning and voice box mechanism (no longer
operational), cotton dress
15 ³/₄"
0-10-49
Museum Purchase, 1953-99

Fig. 96
Detail of Two-Faced Doll
0-10-49
This special doll was patented in Germany and the
United States by Fritz Bartenstein in 1880-81. The
moveable double-faced head with one side smiling
and the other side screaming is turned on a vertical
axis with a metal rod protruding through the top of
the head, underneath the fabric cap. In addition, two
cords on the left side of the body (not extant on this
example) operate the internal voice box which,
according to contemporary descriptions, alternates
with "mama" and a realistic baby cry presumably
designed to accompany the happy and sad faces
respectively. The papier-mâché shoulder plate has a
molded collar and flat frill down the front to the
bust edge.

Fig. 97
Lady
Possibly French
About 1830
Poured-beeswax shoulder head, blonde
human hair inserted in clumps, blue threaded-glass eyes, molded eyelids, painted features, cloth unjointed body, poured-wax
lower arms and legs, damask skirt, silk jacket, lace jabot, black felt hat and slippers,
original cotton pantalets and petticoat
h 13 ¹/₂"
20-10-40a
Chandler Collection, 1962-262.29

Girl
English
About 1800
Poured-beeswax shoulder head with deep
molding at chest, silk floss hair, painted features, cloth swing-jointed body with wax
lower limbs, original tarlatan dress, silk
apron, straw cap
h 6 ¹/₄"
20-10-40b
Chandler Collection, 1962-262.30

These two early nineteenth-century wax doll
are remarkable for their original garments,
complete with hats decorated with feathers
and silk flowers, clothing trimmed with
metal braid, balls and sequins, and cotton
chemise, pantalets, and petticoats.

Fig. 98
Boy
Unknown origin
Unknown date
Wax-over-carved-wooden shoulder head, carved painted blonde hair, brown glass eyes, cloth unjointed body, wooden lower limbs, original silk topcoat and breeches, velvet vest
h 18 1/2"
20-10-43b
Chandler Collection, 1962-262.35

Girl
Unknown origin
Unknown date
Wax-over-composition or plaster shoulder head, pierced ears, glass earrings and necklace, blonde mohair wig, blue glass eyes, kid unjointed body with wooden lower limbs, original silk dress and bonnet, molded wax over plaster basket
h 18 1/4"'
20-10-43a
Chandler Collection, 1962-262.34

The date and origin of this pair of dolls is somewhat of an enigma. The girl doll's wax-over-plaster or -composition head suggests a late nineteenth-century date, while the boy's wax-over-carved-wooden head is of earlier origin. These features are combined with their lower wooden limbs, associated with early papier-mâché dolls. Both the boy and the girl wear their original costumes.

Fig. 99
Quaker Couple
Pennsylvania
About 1830
Carved wax heads, molded noses and mouths, stuffed cloth bodies, wax hands, reed legs covered in cloth, original "Quaker" costumes
6 1/2"
20-10-42ab
Chandler Collection, 1962-262.32 and 33

These handmade folk art dolls were created out of solid carved wax with molded facial features. The woman's silk dress and bonnet, net shawl, cap as well as the man's homespun woolen waistcoat, coat, knee breeches, wool hat, and silk stockings are original.

China Dolls

The great European porcelain-making tradition that began at Meissen, Germany, in 1710 eventually helped establish Germany as the world's leading producer of China doll heads during the nineteenth century. The first "chinas" (vernacular for glazed porcelain dolls), were made at the Königliche Porzellan Manufaktur (KPM) at Meissen and Berlin from 1836 and 1840, respectively. Beginning in the 1840s, the industry was centered chiefly in the state called Thuringia in the cities of Sonneburg, Waltershausen, and Ohrdruf in such factories as Alt, Beck & Gottschalck; Conta & Böhme; Kestner & Co.; A.W. Fr. Kister; C.F. Kling & Co.; Kloster Veilsdorf; and Hertwig & Co.

Aside from its fragility, porcelain proved to be a wonderful medium for doll heads because it could be finely molded. It continued to be used for play dolls until the 1930s. However, by the 1870s and 1880s bisque dolls, made of unglazed, flesh-tinted porcelain, were favored over glazed porcelain dolls partly because the appearance of the material was softer, more lifelike, and thus more appealing than that of the glossy ceramic. Porcelain dolls were made of a translucent body composed of kaolin clay, feldspar, and silica, and doll makers employed two manufacturing methods. Prior to 1860, in press molding, they rolled clay into squares and pressed it into two-part plaster molds for heads. The resulting surface was uneven in thickness and the interior rough. In slip casting—in general usage by 1890—they poured a liquid clay mixture into these molds, which left a surface with uniform thickness and smooth interior.

continued on next page

g. 100
ady
erlin, Germany
ttributed to KPM (Königliche Porzellan Manufaktur, King's Porcelain Factory)
844-47
tamped inside shoulder plate in underglaze blue: German eagle inside circle
ink-tint china shoulder head, molded painted brown hair with center part pulled
ack onto a flat bun, painted blue eyes, orange line running along edge of eyelid
to corner, large red dot completely covering nostril holes, kid swing-jointed body
ith separate fingers, redressed by Marta Mengis in old fabric in 1962, leather
oots
22 ¹/₂"
)-02-74
handler Collection, 1962-262.76

1710 the Königliche Porzellan Manufaktur of Meissen, Germany, was the first European company to produce true hard-paste porcelain sing kaolin clay. KPM primarily supplied expensive luxury items for royalty and the wealthy classes. By 1840, the KPM factory at Berlin started making the finest-quality china-head dolls,[1] such as this serious lady with sensitive modeling, striking face painting, and a rich glaze.

Whichever method was employed, the heads dried in the molds in large, centrally heated rooms until "leather" har and then were removed and allowed to air dry until hard. They then received a thorough sanding by hand to remov mold lines and surface imperfections. The first glaze coat was applied and fired at a high kiln temperature. The facia features were then hand painted onto the glazed surface and the heads reglazed and fired at a lower temperature t set the facial colors. Based on surviving shards Mary Krombholz has discovered, the Thuringian porcelain factorie glazed the head before painting the face and hair. In this sequence, if the inexperienced apprentice made an error, could more easily be removed from the impermeable glazed surface.[2] *Harper's Bazaar* described the manufacturin process in its November 22, 1884, issue:

China dolls are more exclusively the product of a factory. After being modeled by hand, they are baked in a grea oven for a week. During this time, the utmost care and watchfulness are required. The tenders are never permit ted to sleep. A draught of air will produce disastrous results. A single oven contains 5,000 dolls, and thirty oven are often full at once in one factory. At the end of the week the dolls come out in all conditions. About one i five is perfect. After baking, the dolls are painted and glazed. The imperfect ones are separated by themselves an sold to "fairs" and "cheap-john" concerns, which dispose of them to people who infest such places. One Germa factory has been running about one hundred and thirty years, and has produced about one billion dolls.

Available in many sizes, heads were usually sold separately to be joined to various types of cloth, kid or even peg wooden bodies, both made commercially or at home. For the most part, china limbs which are original to the bod can be identified as either child's (rounder and thicker, chubby) or lady's (longer and more slender). However, mo arms and legs of the 1880s were short and round (so-called "bulbous") for both women and children. Dolls made pri to 1860 often have spoon-like china hands and china slippers with flat soles painted red or orange. However, the low arms of the 1890s were identically shaped and could be used interchangeably on the left or right side of the body Later shoes represent higher-heeled boots painted a variety of colors. Often fancy garters have been painted on th stockings. Formal-looking ladies with black molded hair and blue eyes predominated until the 1880s when blue-eye blondes became more common than before. Men with side-parts and children with short necks and windblown ha were produced less frequently. A red line indicating the eyelid and red dots in the corners of the eyes and red dots circles in the nostrils are usually found on the older dolls but are conspicuously missing on the later and less exper sive models of the 1880s. China heads with a pink-tinted complexion, molded bonnets, mohair wigs, or a bald hea made for a wig and those with set glass rather than painted eyes and pierced ears are rarer models.

While the vast majority of china shoulder heads are unmarked, Mary Krombholz has identified distinctive painting fea tures of eyes and mouth that resemble recently excavated factory shards as well as printed sample books. These char acteristics can help attribute specific doll heads to individual porcelain companies.[4] The majority of china dolls ca often be dated by the peak popularity of the European hairstyles that popular period publications such as *Godey Lady's Book* and *Harper's Bazaar* illustrated and helped to disseminate in the United States. However, sought-after dol continued to be produced for decades and thus featured out-of-date coiffures. Within each style many variations occu in the molds in terms of amount and kind of ear exposure; width and length of curls; height, shape, and location o buns; and presence or absence of coronets or snoods (hairnets). Some dolls have distinctive "dos" that are thought t bear a resemblance to the hairstyles of such period celebrities as Dolly Madison, Mary Todd Lincoln, and Jenny Lin although the faces were not originally modeled as realistic portraits of these women. Others have been assigned name for easier identification by collectors, such as "Lydia," "Sophia Smith," "covered wagon," "flat-top," "low brow," "spill curls." Quite often the more popular china heads have been cast in the same molds as other ceramic materi such as bisque or parian-type (untinted, unglazed porcelain).

g. 101
ady
hrdruf, Thuringia, Germany
ttributed to Kestner & Co.
bout 1850
arked in black ink on back shoulder plate:
e
nk-tint china shoulder head, molded paint-
d black hair ("Lydia" style), painted brown
es with white highlights, red eyelid line
d red dot in nostrils, black eyelash line,
ndmade cloth swing-jointed body with
tten hands, redressed in 1964 by Marta
engis using old fabric
12 ³/₄"
-02-05
ebb Collection, 1952-60

Lady
Ohrdruf, Thuringia, Germany
Attributed to Kestner & Co.
About 1850
Incised inside shoulder plate: 12
Pink-tint china shoulder head with molded
bosom, molded painted black hair ("Lydia"
style), painted blue eyes with white highlights, red eyelid line, red dot in corners and
in nostrils, black eyelash line, manufactured
cloth swing-jointed body with leather lower
arms and separate fingers, old cotton dress
h 15 ¹/₂"
20-02-01
Webb Collection, 1952-60

Girl
Ohrdruf, Thuringia, Germany
Attributed to Kestner & Co.
About 1850
Incised under glaze on back shoulder plate
in script: GL
Pink-tint china shoulder head, molded painted black hair ("Sophia Smith" style), painted
brown eyes, red eyelid line, red dot in corners and in nostrils, black eyelash line along
entire lid, handmade cloth swing-jointed
body with kid arms with separate fingers,
original silk dress
h 15 ¹/₂"
20-02-29
Webb Collection, 1952-60

These three dolls share what later collectors termed the "Lydia" and closely related "Sophia
Smith"-type hairstyles actually popular in the 1850s, as the image of Ionie Dutton illustrates.
While both coiffures are characterized by a center part and long vertical curls starting at the
ears, the style is called the "Lydia" if the ringlets fall onto or below the shoulder and the
"Sophia Smith" if the ringlets end abruptly above the neck. Other early features of these
dolls include their pink-tinted complexion and detailed face painting, seen in the black eyelashes, red eyelid lines, and red accent dots in the corners of the eyes and nostrils. All have
been attributed to Kestner & Co. due to the slight unpainted space between the lips, the
unpainted center-part line in the hair, and the white highlight on the left side of the iris.[5]
Furthermore, two of these ladies have the more rare brown painted eyes.

Fig. 102
Ionie Dutton, Age 12, with Lydia Hairstyle
Albumen print
About 1858
Shelburne Museum, 27.12.2-142
G 1997.4.3

Fig. 103
Girl
Scheibe-Alsbach, Thuringia,
Germany
Attributed to A.W. Fr. Kister
About 1840
Pink-tint china shoulder head,
molded painted hair ("covered
wagon" style), painted blue eyes
with red eyelid line, red dot in
corners, manufactured cloth
swing-jointed body with leather
arms, cotton dress
h 22"
20-02-69
Chandler Collection, 1962-262.71

Lady
Veilsdorf, Thuringia, Germany
Attributed to Kloster Veilsdorf
About 1850
China shoulder head, molded
painted black hair ("Greiner"
style), brown glass eyes with red
eyelid line, red dot in corners,
painted upper and lower lashes,
molded ears, cloth swing-jointed
body with lower china arms,
dressed in corset marked "Royal
Worcester/Doll's/Corset 6," cotton underwear, dress and leather
shoes
h 21"
20-02-34
Webb Collection, 1952-60

Girl
Ohrdruf, Thuringia, Germany
Attributed to Kestner & Co.
About 1840
Marked on inside back shoulder
plate: 12x
Pink-tint shoulder head, molded
painted black hair ("covered
wagon" style), painted blue eyes
with white highlights, red eyelid
line, red dot in corners, homemade cloth swing-jointed body
with leather arms and separate
fingers, old cotton dress
h 20"
20-02-20
Webb Collection, 1952-60

Girl
Ohrdruf, Thuringia, Germany
Attributed to Kestner & Co.
About 1840
Marked in black ink inside
shoulder plate: 10/0/2 71/1
Pink-tint shoulder head, molde
painted black hair ("covered
wagon" style), painted brown
eyes with white highlights, red
eyelid line, red dot in corners,
red circle in nostrils, handmade
cloth swing-jointed body with
leather arms and separate fingers, cotton dress, leather shoe
h 21"
20-02-30
Gift of Mrs. J. Ford Johnson,
1953-1177

Three of these dolls share the popular "covered wagon" hairstyle shown in illustrations appearing in *Godey's Lady's Book* in 1848 and charac
terized by a center part high on the forehead pulled down smoothly over the ears with corkscrew curls all the way around the back of the
head. The style is found primarily on dolls that represent young girls and teenagers from the 1840s through the 1850s. The name "covered
wagon" clearly refers to the wagon trains traveling west and reflects the simple hairstyle of American women and their daughters depicted i
period daguerreotypes. The doll with the closely related "Greiner" coiffure (20-02-34) shows a style named for its similarity to the America
papier-mâché dolls made by Ludwig Greiner, with a center part waved to the back of deeply molded exposed ears and vertical curls adhering
closely around the back of the head. The eyelashes are often individually painted with small, even brushstrokes. Such dolls often have the
much rarer glass eyes.

g. 104
rl
heibe-Alsbach, Thuringia, Germany
tributed to A.W. Fr. Kister
out 1840
hina shoulder head, molded painted black
ir ("covered wagon" style), painted blue
es, red eyelid lines, red dot in corners and
nostrils, peg-wooden jointed body with
wer china limbs, five fingers on right hand
rled around to hold object, four fingers
d separated thumb on left hand, flat feet
th painted orange shoes, original gauze
ess
11 1/2"
-02-31
ebb Collection, 1952-60

rl
heibe-Alsbach, Thuringia, Germany
tributed to A.W. Fr. Kister
out 1860-70
nk-tint china shoulder head, molded paint-
black hair ("covered wagon" style), paint-
brown eyes, red eyelid line, red dot in
rners, and in nostrils, cloth swing-jointed
dy with lower china limbs, mitten hands
th separate thumb, gold luster boots
inted on with slight heel, silk dress
5 1/2"
-02-15
ebb Collection, 1952-60

Girl
Ohrdruf, Thuringia, Germany
Attributed to Kestner & Co.
About 1850
China shoulder head, molded painted black
hair ("covered wagon" style), painted brown
eyes, red eyelid lines, red dot in corners and
in nostrils, manufactured cloth swing-jointed
body with lower china limbs, flat feet with
painted-on black slippers, original dress
h 9 1/2"
20-02-68
Chandler Collection, 1962-262.70

Girl
Scheibe-Alsbach, Thuringia, Germany
Attributed to A.W. Fr. Kister
About 184
Pink-tint china shoulder head, molded painted black hair, painted brown eyes, red eyelid
lines, red dot in nostrils, peg jointed wooden
body with lower china limbs, right hand
molded into a circle, left hand mitten with
separate thumb, flat orange painted slippers, silk skirt
h 5 1/4"
20-02-14
Webb Collection, 1952-60

Girl
Veilsdorf, Thuringia, Germany
Attributed to Kloster Veilsdorf
About 1840
Pink-tint china shoulder head, molded painted black hair ("Greiner" style), painted blue
eyes, red eyelid lines, red dot in corners and
in nostrils, cloth swing-jointed body with
lower leather arms, mitten hands, and four
separate fingers sticking out at end, cotton
dress
h 13 1/2"
20-02-58
Chandler Collection, 1962-262.59

While four of these dolls share the "covered
wagon" and closely related "Greiner" style
coiffure, Kister factory products (20-02-31
and 20-02-14) are distinguished by the more
unusual articulated peg-jointed wooden
body with the right china hand molded in a
circle to grasp accessories such as flowers, a
handkerchief, or a parasol.[6]

Fig. 105
Girl (one of twin)
Scheibe-Alsbach, Thuringia, Germany
Attributed to A.W. Fr. Kister
About 1860-70
China shoulder head, molded painted black
hair ("high-brow" style), painted blue eyes,
red eyelid line, painted bow mouth, handmade cloth swing-jointed body with mitten
hands, original cotton plaid dress, apron,
petticoat, pantalets, leather shoes
h 10"
20-02-09a
Webb Collection, 1952-60

Girl
Scheibe-Alsbach, Thuringia, Germany
Attributed to A.W. Fr. Kister
About 1860-70
China shoulder head, molded and painted
black hair ("flat-top"style), painted blue eyes,
red dot in nostrils, painted mouth, manufactured cloth swing-jointed body with lower
china limbs, black flat-heeled china boots,
original lace and lawn dress and cotton
underwear
h 7 3/4"
20-02-10
Webb Collection, 1952-60

Girl
Katzhütte, Thuringia, Germany
Attributed to Hertwig & Co.
About 1870
China shoulder head, molded painted black
hair ("flat-top" style), squash-shaped head,
painted blue eyes glancing upward to right,
cloth swing-jointed body with lower china
limbs and gold-painted china boots, cotton
chemise and petticoat
h 10"
20-02-47
Chandler Collection, 1962-262.48

Girl
Nauendorf, Thuringia, Germany
Attributed to Alt, Beck & Gottschalck
About 1860-70
China shoulder head, molded painted black
hair ("flat-top" style), painted blue eyes,
manufactured cloth swing-jointed body,
lower china limbs with black flat-heeled
china boots, velvet and lace dress
h 7 3/4"
20-02-38
Gift of Dr. and Mrs. J. W. Willcox, 1954-127.1

All these dolls exhibit the "flat-top" or closely related "high brow" coiffure appearing in
Godey's Lady's Book in 1862. The flat top is
distinguished by flat curls emanating from a
central part, the curls framing the face clos-
ly. The "high brow" coiffure featured a high
center part with very smooth hair drawn
back to reveal much of the forehead, and
flaring out at the sides to form short ringlet
over the ears and around the head. The two
girl dolls on the left have their original,
hand-stitched clothing, while the doll on
their right is dressed in cotton undergarments. She is an example of a less expensi
doll with a squash-shaped head and a minimum of painted facial detail.

Fig. 106
Girl
Ohrdruf, Thuringia, Germany
Attributed to Kestner & Co.
About 1860-70
Marked inside back shoulder plate: 15
China shoulder head, molded painted black
hair ("flat-top" style), painted blue eyes with
white highlights, red eyelid lines, red dot in
corners and in nostrils, homemade cloth
body swing-jointed at hips and shoulders,
separately stitched cloth fingers, cotton
dress with apron
h 28 1/4"
20-02-79
Estate of Bernice Cox, 1954-395

Girl
Nauendorf, Thuringia, Germany
Attributed to Alt, Beck & Gottschalck
About 1860-70
China shoulder head, molded painted black
hair parted in center with short curls around
sides and in back, with molded ribbon and
bow in center on top ("Dolly Madison"
style), painted blue eyes with white highlights, red eyelid lines, red dot in corners
and in nostrils, cloth swing-jointed body
with leather arms and fingers stiffened with
dowels, cotton petticoat, pantalets, and
chemise
h 33 3/8"
20-02-27
Webb Collection, 1952-60

Girl
Nauendorf, Thuringia, Germany
Attributed to Alt, Beck & Gottschalck
About 1860-70
Marked inside shoulder plate: 75
China shoulder head, molded painted black
hair ("flat-top" style), painted blue eyes with
white highlights, red eyelid lines, red dot in
corners and in nostrils, manufactured cloth
swing-jointed body at hips, knees, and
shoulders, lower kid arms with five stitched
fingers and stitched toes, cotton petticoat
and chemise
h 24 1/4"
20-02-28
Webb Collection, 1952-60

Girl
Scheibe-Alsbach, Thuringia, Germany
Attributed to A.W. Fr. Kister
About 1860-70
Incised on front shoulder plate: 13
China shoulder head, molded painted black
hair ("flat-top" style), painted blue eyes, red
eyelid lines, manufactured cloth swing-jointed body at hips, knees, and shoulders with
lower kid arms, five stitched leather fingers
and stitched toes, cotton pantalets and
chemise
h 24 1/4"
20-02-33
Webb Collection, 1952-60

These large china shoulder head dolls,
measuring more than twenty-four inches
high, wear various combinations of the
same three basic pieces of underclothing—
the chemise, petticoat, and drawers. All of
these clothing items originally were a proper
part of man's attire—namely, chemise, or
the Norman name for shirt; "petit coat," the
Middle Age term for little coat; and drawers,
which originated as "pantaloons" or pants in
the early nineteenth century. In actual
clothes copied for dolls, the underpants with
straight legs were gathered at the top with
string or cloth tape or into a waistband and
buttoned. Most extended below the knees, a
few were at midcalf, and several ran to the
shoe tops and were often bordered with lace
or trimmed with rows of tucks. According to
The Handbook of the Toilet (1841). "The
drawers of ladies may be made of flannel,
Angola, calico or even cotton stocking-web;
they should reach down the leg as far as it is
possible to make them without their being
seen."[7]

Fig. 107
Girl
Scheibe-Alsbach, Thuringia, Germany
Attributed to A.W. Fr. Kister
About 1850
Pink-tint china shoulder head, molded painted black hair ("flat-top" style), painted blue eyes, red eyelid lines, red dot in corners, manufactured cloth swing-jointed body with china lower limbs, leather feet, cotton chemise, petticoat, and pantalets
h 21 ½"
20-02-56
Chandler Collection, 1962-262.57

Lady
Veilsdorf, Thuringia, Germany
Attributed to Kloster Veilsdorf
About 1850
Incised inside back shoulder plate: 16
China shoulder head, molded painted black hair ("flat-top" style), painted brown eyes with white highlights, deeply molded curls, eyes, nose, lips, and cheeks, brush-stroked brows and lower lashes, red eyelid lines, red dot in corners, red circle in nostrils, manufactured cloth swing-jointed body with leather arms, cotton chemise, petticoat, pantalets
h 28"
20-02-41
Museum Purchase, 1959-221.3

Lady
Denmark
Royal Copenhagen
About 1840-50
Marked in underglaze blue on inside back shoulder in underglaze blue: three parallel lines
China shoulder head, molded painted black hair center parted with sides dipped down around exposed with chignon at middle on back of head, ("Queen Victoria" style), painted blue eyes, red eyelid line, red dot in nostrils, unjointed cotton-covered kid body, bone arms and fingers, cotton pantalets, petticoat with rickrack trim, and corset hooked in front
h 16"
20-02-72
Chandler Collection, 1962-262.74

Lady
Veilsdorf, Thuringia, Germany
Attibuted to Kloster Veilsdorf
About 1850
China shoulder head, molded painted black hair ("Greiner" style), brown glass eyes, red eyelid lines, red dot in corners, upper and lower lashes, molded ears, cloth swing-jointed body with lower china arms, dressed in corset marked "Royal Worcester/Doll's/Corset 6"
h 21"
20-02-34
Webb Collection, 1952-60

Dolls' undergarments copied adult models. Four to six petticoats were worn according to the season. Only the outermost—of which a woman might allow glimpses at her discretion—was in any sense decorative, elaborately trimmed with lace, embroidery, or rickrack several inches above the hem. The tiny waist reflects a most important fashion statement that helped to define every woman's femininity throughout the nineteenth century. The style of corsets, which were a part of women's and even children's dress since the 1600s, vacillated over time. They ranged from short to long, had or lacked shoulder straps, featured either front or back lacing, and could be fitted with cord or bone stiffenings.

The Royal Worcester Corset Company in Worcester, Massachusetts, was the leading manufacturer of women's foundation garments in the United States, England, and Australia from 1861 to 1950. The lady on the right wears a rare example of a doll-size version of their "Dress Form" model, made for adults from 1892 to 1898.[8]

Fig. 108
Girl
Nauendorf, Thuringia, Germany
Attributed to Alt, Beck &
Gottschalck
About 1860-70
Incised inside shoulder plate: G
Pink-tint china shoulder head,
molded painted black hair ("high-
brow" style), painted blue eyes
with highlights, red eyelid lines,
red dot in corners, circle dot in
nostrils, manufactured cloth
swing-jointed body with lower
leather arms, cotton dress, leather
shoes
h 23 1/4"
20-02-26
Webb Collection, 1952-60

Girl
Scheibe-Alsbach, Thuringia,
Germany
Attributed to A.W. Fr. Kister
About 1860-70
China shoulder head, molded
painted black hair ("high-brow"
style), painted blue eyes, red eyelid
lines, red dot in nostrils, manufactured cloth swing-jointed body
with leather arms and hands with
five separate fingers (not original
to head), attached leather boots
h 16"
20-02-84
Museum Purchase, 1953-1033.1

Girl
Ohrdruf, Thuringia, Germany
Attributed to Kestner & Co.
About 1860-70
China shoulder head, molded
painted black hair ("high-brow"
style), painted blue eyes with white
highlights, peach eyelid lines, red
dot in corners and in nostrils,
manufactured cloth swing-jointed
body with kid arms and hands with
separate fingers, one original china
leg with garter and orange boot,
and wooden carved right leg (not
original to body)
h 20"
20-02-43
Chandler Collection, 1962-262.44

All three of these girls have tightly
stuffed, manufactured cloth bodies
with wide hips and narrow waists.
The lower limbs can be of cloth,
china, or leather, as in these examples. More unusual are the leather
boots sewn onto the doll at center.
The girl at right is unique with her
old hand-carved replacement right
leg designed to match the original
left china leg exactly—including
the orange heeled boot, bulbous
calf, and even blue garter with a
bow.

ig. 109
ady
ermany
bout 1870
ink-tint china shoulder head, molded
ainted black hair with center part and
hort all-over curls, painted blue eyes
ith white highlights and heavily mold-
d lids, thick black eyeliner on lids end-
g in red dot in corners and in nostrils,
pen/closed mouth with painted teeth,
ateen swing-jointed body (not original)
ith old deeply molded china hands
ith molded knuckles and traces of red-
ainted nails, old voile dress made by
rs. George Chandler, leather slippers
 28"
-02-77
handler Collection, 1962-262.79

his distinguished portrait-type bride
as a striking "Mona Lisa" smile and
pen mouth closed at the rear with
nusual molded teeth. Her eye and lid

painting is very dramatic and theatrical
and unlike any other doll models from
identified German factories. Her carefully molded hands were probably
secured to the leather arms using a
patent by Martin Kintzback of
Philadelphia, who invented "an
Improved Manner of Fastening the
Hands of Dolls into the Arms of the
same" (#95,489) in 1869. This resulted
in a very neat joining using a cork to
conceal the rough edges of the leather
arm as it is tied and glued around the
porcelain hand, although Kintzback did
not claim to make these distinctive
china hands.[9] The identical hand and
interface is also seen on a parian-type
doll in the Shelburne Museum collection (fig. 157). This costume, made
from old material by Mrs. George
Chandler, won a blue ribbon at the
eighth annual doll exhibit at the Powers
Memorial Museum in 1947.

Fig. 110
Lady
Berlin, Germany
KPM (Königliche Porzellan Manufaktur,
King's Porcelain Factory)
About 1840-44
Stamped in underglaze blue on inside front
shoulder plate: German eagle
China shoulder head, molded painted brown
hair with center part swept down around
face and gathered into a bun, painted blue
eyes, homemade cloth unjointed body with
wooden hands, cotton dress
h 12"
20-02-04
Webb Collection, 1952-60

Lady
Berlin, Germany
KPM (Königliche Porzellan Manufaktur,
King's Porcelain Factory)
About 1844-47
Stamped in underglaze blue on inside front
shoulder plate: German eagle inside circle
Pink-tint china shoulder head, molded painted brown hair with center part pulled back
into a flat bun, painted blue eyes, orange
line running along edge of eyelid into corner,
large red dot completely covering nostril
holes, kid swing-jointed body with separate
fingers, redressed by Marta Mengis in old
fabric in 1963, leather boots
h 22 1/2"
20-02-74
Chandler Collection, 1962-262.76

Gentleman
Berlin, Germany
KPM (Königliche Porzellan Manufaktur,
King's Porcelain Factory)
About 1844-47
Stamped in underglaze blue on inside front
shoulder plate: German eagle inside circle
Pink-tint china shoulder head, molded painted brown hair in left side part and exposed
ears with bangs at one side, painted blue
eyes, orange line running along edge of
heavily molded eyelid into corner, sateen
body with lower china arms, silk costume
h 18 1/2"
20-02-75
Chandler Collection, 1962-262.77

With their superb sculpting and lifelike facial painting, these KPM dolls have an aristocratic expression and look as though they might be portraits of real people. The natural, pink-tinted complexion and heavily molded eyelids provide a realistic appearance. All three exhibit unusual pointed and painted orange eyeliner and the much rarer chocolate brown rather than black hair. The women with smoothly shaped hair and flat bun and the rare man with characteristic side part have restrained yet elegant coiffures. These china dolls produced in the 1840 set a standard of excellence unequalled by other porcelain factories.[10]

Fig. 111

Lady
Pössneck, Thuringia, Germany
Attributed to Conta & Böhme
About 1860
Incised on outside back of shoulder plate: 11
China shoulder head with pierced ears and
donut-shaped earring, molded painted black
hair with brush strokes around face into
wings at side with band across top of head
holding back bun of curls, painted blue eyes,
red eyelid line, red dot in corners and in
nostrils, manufactured cloth swing-jointed
body with china lower limbs, old velvet and
silk costume
h 22"
20-02-03
Webb Collection, 1952-60

Lady
Pössneck, Thuringia, Germany
Attributed to Conta & Böhme
About 1860-70
China shoulder head, molded and painted
black hair with brush marks around face
swept back into wings on sides and pulled
up in back and secured with comb, painted
blue eyes, red eyelid line, red dot in corners
and in nostrils, cloth swing-jointed body
with lower leather forearms and china
hands, silk and lace costume
h 13 3/4"
20-02-06
Webb Collection, 1952-60

Girl
Pössneck, Thuringia, Germany
Attributed to Conta & Böhme
About 1870-80
Incised on outside of shoulder plate: 6
Incised on inside of shoulder plate : 5
China shoulder head, molded painted black
hair with brush marks at side and puffs over
forehead, brush marks around hairline and
circle of puffs tied with molded ribbon at
back, painted blue eyes, red eyelid line, red
dot in corners and in nostrils, homemade
cloth swing-jointed body with lower china
limbs and orange heeled boots, old silk
costume
h 21 1/2"
20-02-35
Webb Collection, 1952-60

Girl
Pössneck, Thuringia, Germany
Attributed to Conta & Böhme
About 1860-70
Pink-tint china shoulder head, molded paint-
ed black hair with brush marks around face,
exposed ears and curls in back, painted blue
eyes, red eyelid line, red dot in nostrils,

manufactured cloth swing-jointed body with
lower china limbs, cotton and silk costume
with velvet ribbons
h 14 1/2"
20-02-53
Chandler Collection, 1962-262.54

Lady
Pössneck, Thuringia, Germany
Attributed to Conta & Böhme
About 1860-70
China shoulder head, molded painted black
hair with waves over forehead, band across
center of head and sausage curls in back,
pierced ears, painted blue eyes, red dot in
nostrils, cloth swing-jointed body with lower
china limbs and flat feet, black-painted
shoes, old cotton print dress
h 12 1/2"
20-02-66
Chandler Collection, 1962-262.68

Lady
Pössneck, Thuringia, Germany
Attributed to Conta & Böhme
About 1870-80
Remains of blue label on body: n7
Painted in black on inside back of shoulder
plate: 6w
China shoulder head, molded painted black
hair with brush marks at temples and center
part waved to sides with braided coronet,
painted blue eyes, red eyelid lines, red dot in
corners and in nostrils, manufactured kid
swing-jointed body, brocade costume
h 20 3/4'
20-02-61
Chandler Collection, 1962-262.63

Lady
Pössneck, Thuringia, Germany
Attributed to Conta & Böhme
About 1860-70
China shoulder head with large pierced ear-
hole and donut shaped earrings, molded
painted black hair, off-center curl at forehead
with wings at side and bun of curls in back
("Countess Dagmar" style), painted blue
eyes, red eyelid line, homemade homespun
unjointed body with kid arms, new kid
hands, old cotton dress
h 18 1/2"
20-02-60
Chandler Collection, 1961.262.62

By 1870, girls and ladies show a variety of
elaborate hairstyles with detailed molding.
Many exhibit brush strokes at the temples
combined with waves, braids, twists, puffs,
and combs as well as pierced ears and earrings.[11] The "Countess Dagmar" hairstyle,
displayed on the doll at far right, is named
for the mother of Nicholas II, last czar of
Russia. New research by Mary Krombholz
based on excavated factory shards and sample books enables the attribution of all of
these unmarked heads to the German factories of Conta & Böhme, founded in 1790.[12]
They exhibit eyes that have a sleepy look
with the pupils painted right below the eyelid line, larger mouths curled up at the corners with a visible space between the lips,
and ears pierced with large slits rather than
a round hole.

Fig. 112
Lady
Pössneck, Thuringia, Germany
Attributed to Conta & Böhme
About 1860
Incised inside shoulder plate: 6
China shoulder head, molded painted black hair, painted blue eyes, manufactured cloth swing-jointed body with lower leather arms, old silk dress
h 21 ½"
20-02-71
Chandler Collection, 1962-262.73

This doll's painted hair has exquisite detail, showing tiny brush marks at the hairline framing the face. It is swept into wide wings on the sides, pulled up to the middle of the head in back, and held in place by a semicircular molded comb. This model depicts a distinguished woman with an aquiline nose and enigmatic smile whose features are lifelike rather than doll-like.[13]

Fig. 113
Lady
Ohrdruf, Thuringia, Germany
Attributed to Kestner & Co.
About 1860-70
Incised in front under shoulder plate: h
China shoulder head, molded painted black hair ("Mary Todd" style), painted blue eyes with highlights, peach eyelid line, peach dot in corners and peach circles in nostrils, replaced kid fashion body with gusset joints and old china lower limbs, redressed by Mrs. F. C. Jeffries
h 17 ½"
20-02-63
Chandler Collection, 1962-262.65

Lady
Ohrdruf, Thuringia, Germany
Kestner & Co.[14]
About 1860-70
China shoulder head, molded painted black hair ("grape lady" style), painted blue eyes, red eyelid line, red dot in nostrils, homemade cloth swing-jointed body, old silk costume
h 15 ¾"
20-02-64
Chandler Collection, 1961-262.66

The hairstyle of the lady on the left, known as "Mary Todd" in America, was named after President Abraham Lincoln's wife, prominent because of her husband's role during the Civil War. It is distinguished by modeled bows at each side and a hair band over a center part with a fine net called a snood at the back of the head.

The so-called "grape lady" on the right also has an imaginative ornamental coiffure consisting of a molded white ruffle on both sides of the head forming a band over the ears and meeting at the top of the head in a central cluster of five blue grapes. Her pageboy at the rear is caught in a gold luster snood.

Fig. 114
Lady
Pössneck, Thuringia, Germany
Attributed to Conta & Böhme
About 1860-70
Pink-tint china shoulder head,
molded painted black hair coiled
around face and into braided bun,
painted blue eyes, slight lines over
eyes, dots in corner and in nostrils,
homemade cloth swing-jointed
body, cloth mitten hands, redressed
by Mrs. George Chandler
h 14"
20-02-55
Chandler Collection, 1961-262.56

Lady
Pössneck, Thuringia, Germany
Attributed to Conta & Böhme
About 1860-70
Incised on shoulder plate: 141 or
131 painted over in red 87
China shoulder head, molded
painted black hair with waves in
front and forming roll around face,
braid across top of head and three
sausage curls in back at neck
("waterfall" style) painted blue eyes,
red lines over lids, dots in corners
and in nostrils, manufactured cloth
swing-jointed body with stump
arms (no hands), newly made
dress by Marta Mengis in early
1960s, old cotton underwear, silk
boots
h 19"
20-02-70
Chandler Collection, 1961-262.72

According to a 1904 description of women's fashions, "A prevalent style of coiffure during the ten years between 1860 and 1870 was popularly known as the waterfall. A frame of horsehair was attached to the back of the head by an elastic, and the back hair was brushed smoothly over it, the ends caught up underneath. A net was usually worn over this chignon to keep the hair in place. Often the whole structure was made of false hair and fastened on with hairpins."[15] Snoods or hairnets, which covered the back of a woman's hair, were often worn to keep a waterfall hairdo in place. A chignon is defined as "a large, smooth twist, roll or knot of hair worn by woman at the nape of the neck"; a bun is "hair gathered in a round coil or knot above the nape of the neck or on top of the head."[16]

Fig. 115
Lady
Scheibe-Alsbach, Thuringia, Germany
Attributed to A.W. Fr. Kister
About 1860-70
China shoulder head, molded painted black hair, painted blue eyes, manufactured cloth swing-jointed body with lower unglazed porcelain limbs
h 12"
20-02-67
Chandler Collection, 1962-262.69

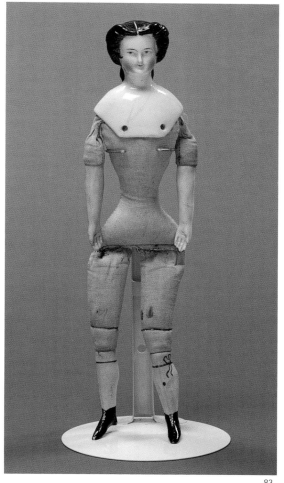

Many unusual doll parts were discarded under the floorboards of the factory of A.W. Fr. Kister founded in Scheibe-Alsbach in 1837. It was difficult to dispose of damaged china in the winter months when the ground was frozen and the imperfect items—or seconds—could not be buried. This unglazed bisque lower leg with its distinctive blue garter bow and the rose-colored crossed laces painted on its flat, tan-soled black boot is identical to documented excavated Kister pieces.[17] The doll has a Kister commercial swing-jointed cloth body made by some factory workers, a china shoulder head with distinctive brush marks around the face, spit curls at the ears, and wings at the sides of the head that are coiled to the back with a fall underneath a semicircular comb.

Fig. 116
Lady
Ohrdruf, Thuringia, Germany
Attributed to Kestner & Co.
About 1860-1870
Incised inside shoulder plate: 9
Decorated china shoulder head, molded painted blonde hair with bows at front ears and snood in back with wide black seam, painted blue eyes, peach eyelid lines, peach dot at corners and in nostrils, old cloth swing-jointed body with lower china limbs and flat feet with black painted boots and red laces, cotton corset, pantalets, chemise, and petticoat
h 22"
20-02-07
Webb Collection, 1952-60

The Grecian figure with high rounded breasts and small waistline was the ideal every woman longed to achieve. In the late 1840s the French introduced a corset without gussets made from seven to thirteen separate pieces, each one being shaped into the waist, similar to the one this lady doll wears. In the 1860s, when the crinoline was at its widest and the main role of the corset was to minimize the waist, this type of boned cotton corset that laces up the back was extremely popular, especially in Europe.[18] The doll's feminine figure is further enhanced by wool padding sewn to her bustline.

Fig. 117
Boy
Possibly French
About 1850
China shoulder head, painted black hair, painted blue eyes with lashes, red dot in corners and in nostrils, cloth French ungusseted body with lower kid arms, sewn into original brocade gown with brass braid, old leather shoes
h 12"
20-02-73
Chandler Collection, 1961-262.75

This unusual male doll—distinguished by short, windblown hair without a part—is probably of French origin with brush marks around the face, painted lashes, and a French-style ungusseted body. He is also dressed in an unusual original, red brocade gown with metal trim, which perhaps was designed to represent a religious or aristocratic costume.

oy
hrdruf, Thuringia, Germany
ttributed to Kestner & Co.
bout 1850
nk-tint china shoulder head, molded paint-
d black hair, painted blue eyes, red lid lines,
d dot in corners, manufactured cloth
wing-jointed body, leather arms and boots
23"
-02-32
ebb Collection, 1952-60

oy
heibe-Alsbach, Thuringia, Germany
ttributed to A.W. Fr. Kister
bout 1850-1900
cised on bottom of feet: 14 [on one], 15 [on
e other]
mobile china (badekinder, or so-called
rozen Charlie"), molded painted black
air, painted blue eyes, unjointed china body
ith molded buttocks, navel, elbows, curved
ands with four molded fingers with nails
d separate thumb, never clothed
13 1/2"
-02-40
useum Purchase, 1955-611.2

Gentleman
Ohrdruf, Thuringia, Germany
Attributed to Kestner & Co.[19]
About 1860
China shoulder head, black molded
painted black hair with left side part
and brush marks, painted blue eyes,
red lid lines, red dots in corners,
red circle nose dots, painted mouth
with separation, manufactured cloth
swing-jointed body at shoulder,
hips, and knees, lower carved wood-
en arms with mitten hands and separate thumb
h 24"
20-02-76
Chandler Collection, 1962-262.78

Following the doll head production
at KPM Berlin in 1840, the Kister
and Kestner porcelain factories
manufactured the earliest male heads
during the same decade. The fine brush
marks painted around the hairline of the tall
dolls' faces indicates an early date.[20] Even
undressed, the young boy or kinderkopf at
left with the short neck, round face, chubby
cheeks, and windblown hair without a part
can be distinguished from the adult male at
right with elongated neck, slender, oval face
and side-parted hair. There are also variations
in their professionally manufactured bodies.
Although both have cloth swing joints at the
hips and knees, the arms can be made of
leather with separate fingers or fashioned
from wood with carved mitten hands.

The all-china boy in the center, first produced about 1850, is known as a bathing
doll or badekinder in Germany and was originally intended as a Victorian bath toy
designed to float in water. These one-piece
chubby boys are identified by collectors
today as Frozen Charlies because they are
rigid and have no moving parts. Despite the
fact that these dolls were unlikely playthings
due to their fragility, they were extremely
popular and produced for more than sixty
years in sizes ranging from one to eighteen
inches. This example is relatively common.

Fig. 119
Girl
Katzhütte, Thuringia, Germany
Attributed to Hertwig & Co.
About 1890
Incised on head and all limbs: 0
China shoulder head, molded painted black
hair ("low-brow" style), painted blue eyes,
red dot in nostrils, cloth body with lower
china limbs, wool lace-trimmed dress with
linen chemise, cotton apron, petticoat, and
pantalets
h 10"
20-02-87
Gift of Mrs. Charles Slentz, 1964-80.3

Girl
Katzhütte, Thuringia, Germany
Attributed to Hertwig & Co.
About 1890
Stamped on back of shoulder plate and right
and left arm: 2
China shoulder head, molded painted black
hair ("low-brow" stye), painted blue eyes,
red eyelid lines, red dot in nostrils, manufactured cloth body with lower china limbs,
dressed in old cotton skirt and smock with
cotton pantalets and petticoat printed,
"Manufactured by B.B. & R. Knight,
Providence, R.I." inside hem
h 14 1/2"
20-02-90
Gift of Mrs. M. E. Windhol, 1966-196.1

he Hertwig & Co. porcelain factory probably made this pair of shoulder heads characterized by large, blue painted irises without outline or
hite highlights, heart-shaped mouths with a matching-color straight line separating the upper and lower lips, and generously blushed
eeks.[21] They also share the so-called "low-brow" hairstyle shown in a French fashion plate in the May 1894 issue of *Harper's Bazaar* and
aracterized by wavy hair with a white center part that is very low on the forehead. The majority of "common low brows" lack the definitive
nter part. They were produced in vast quantity and sold cheaply without bodies in the United States for one to ten cents in many sizes,
om ten inches to more than two feet tall.

Fig. 120
Boy
Nauendorf, Thuringia, Germany
Attributed to Alt, Beck & Gottschalck
About 1880
China shoulder head, molded painted black hair, painted blue eyes with white highlights, peach eyelid lines, peach dot in corners and in nostrils, new cloth swing-jointed body with old china hands with four molded fingers and separate thumbs and plaster legs, old wool suit
h 27 ¹/₂"
20-02-59b
Chandler Collection, 1961-262.61

Girl
Nauendorf, Thuringia, Germany
Attributed to Alt, Beck & Gottschalck
About 1880
China shoulder head, molded painted black hair, painted blue eyes with white highlights, peach eyelid lines, peach dot in corners and in nostrils, new cloth swing-jointed body with old china hands with four molded fingers and separate thumb and old bulbous china legs with heeled boots and painted garter, old cotton and lace dress
h 25 ¹/₂"
20-02-59a
Chandler Collection, 1961-262.60

The 1880s was the decade of childlike chinas. Doll heads with elaborate hairstyles were replaced by youthful countenances with short necks, chubby cheeks, round eyes, and masses of curly hair. The Alt, Beck & Gottschalck porcelain factory led the market in creating a variety of molds portraying the new image, depicted in this youthful pair.[22]

Fig. 121
Girl
Nauendorf, Thuringia, Germany
Attributed to Alt, Beck & Gottschalck
About 1850
China shoulder head, bald head with black spot in center ("Biedermeier" type), painted blue eyes, red eyelid lines, red dot in corners and in nostrils, cloth swing-jointed body with lower china limbs, china mitten hands, dressed in silk Amish costume
h 7 ¹/₂"
20-02-45
Chandler Collection, 1962-262.46

Lady
Possibly United States
Unknown date
Glazed redware shoulder head, molded bonnet and facial features, manufactured cloth swing-jointed body with kid arms and mitten fingers with separate thumb, dressed in Quaker cotton costume
h 12 ¹/₄"
20-03-16
Webb Collection, 1952-60

The distinguishing feature of the doll on the left is her smoothly modeled bald head with black-painted ball-indicator for wig placement—however, instead, she is fitted with a cap as part of her Amish costume. These chinas designated to wear separate wigs are often identified as "Biedermeiers," a misnomer because the word pertains to a late neoclassical style of furnishings characterized b unpretentious elegance common in Germany and Austria from the early to mid-nineteenth century.[23] The unique redware shoulder-head do on the right has a molded bonnet complete with ribbon and ties and a dress to complete her Quaker outfit.

Fig. 122

Girl
Nauendorf, Thuringia, Germany
Attributed to Alt, Beck & Gottschalck
About 1880
China shoulder head, molded painted
blonde short curly hair with center part,
painted blue eyes with white highlights, red
eyelid lines, red dot in corners and in nostrils, manufactured cloth swing-jointed body
with lower kid arms and stitched fingers, old
silk and velvet dress, cotton and lace pantalets, petticoat, and chemise
18 ½"
20-02-57
Chandler Collection, 1962-262.58

Girl
Nauendorf, Thuringia, Germany
Attributed to Alt, Beck & Gottschalck
About 1880
China shoulder head, molded painted
blonde hair in all-over wavy style with no
part, painted blue eyes with white highlights,
red eyelid lines, red dot in corners and in
nostrils, new cloth swing-jointed body with
lower china arms, redressed by Mrs. F. C.
Jeffries in silk costume
20 ½"
20-02-50
Chandler Collection, 1962-262.51

Girl
Nauendorf, Thuringia, Germany
Attributed to Alt, Beck & Gottschalck[24]
About 1870
China shoulder head, molded painted
blonde hair in curly style with ribbon encir-
cling head and black bow over center part
("Dolly Madison" style), pierced ears with
gold drop earrings, painted blue eyes, red
eyelid lines, red dot in corners and in nostrils, homemade cloth swing-jointed body
with leather arms and mitten hands with five
stitched fingers, redressed by Mrs. George
Chandler
h 20"
20-02-54
Chandler Collection, 1962-262.55

Lady
Nauendorf, Thuringia, Germany
Attributed to Alt, Beck & Gottschalck[25]
About 1870
China shoulder head, molded and painted
café-au-lait hair with vertical finger curls covering whole head ("curly-top" style), painted
blue eyes, peach eyelid lines, red dots in corners and in nostrils, cloth swing-jointed
body with kid lower arms and separate
stitched fingers, cotton chemise, petticoat,
and pantalets
h 20"
20-02-08
Webb Collection, 1952-60

Girl
Nauendorf, Thuringia, Germany
Attributed to Alt, Beck & Gottschalck[26]
About 1870
China shoulder head, molded and painted
café-au-lait hair with curls around face and
band on top of head and cascade of gradu-
ated finger curls falling back ("spill-curls"
style), painted blue eyes with white highlights, red eyelid line, red dot in corners and
in nostrils, old homemade cloth body with
lower china arms, hands interchangeable,
silk dress
h 22"
20-02-02
Webb Collection, 1952-60

Although chinas diminished in popularity,
the decade of the late 1860s and early 1870s
marked the introduction of a group of dolls
with well-modeled hairstyles based on
Godey's Lady's Book's latest fashion plates of
1867.[27] These blonde, blue-eyed girls have a
variety of curly "dos" that collectors have
referred to as spill curls, curly tops, and
Dolly Madison, the last in reference to the
style worn by the wife of U.S. President
James Madison, in office from 1809 to 1817.
The dating of these dolls (1870) often fails
to coincide with the life span of their name-
sakes.[28] All of these Alt, Beck & Gottschalck
dolls are characterized by chubby cheeks
and a dark line between the lips that dips
down in the middle.

Bisque Dolls

The process of manufacturing bisque doll heads originated about 1860 primarily in France and Germany. This twice-fired but unglazed porcelain called biscuit could be delicately tinted and colored between firings and thus lent itself perfectly to the production of dolls' heads with natural colors and a matte finish. Although they did not immediately or entirely replace glazed china or even papier mâché, bisque-head dolls became so popular that their manufacture in Paris developed into an important industry very quickly.[1]

The French bisque-head lady dolls manufactured between 1860 and 1890 served as luxurious playthings for wealthy children and adults. Often referred to as Parisiennes or *poupées,* they also mirrored the current mode of dress and advertised the country's chic clothing styles internationally. According to Edouard Fournier's *Histoire des Jouets et des Jeux d'Enfants* of 1888, "The Parisian doll is always stylishly dressed and carefully attired according to the latest fashion. . . . It is recognized that without these dolls our fashions might not be spread into many parts of Europe and especially into the countries of America."

While the original purpose of the well-dressed doll might have been to serve as another plaything, it also provided an important educational function. An article in the January 6, 1877, issue of *Harper's Weekly* observed, "Many of the French dolls at the 1876 centennial exposition were furnished with the most elaborate toilets, which the little ladies, who became their owners could change at leisure according to the time of day or the occasion at which the mimic lady was to make her appearance." Furthermore, a daughter's toy also served as a

continued on next page

g. 123
bé
aris and Montreuil-sous-Bois, France
robably Bru Jne. & Cie
bout 1880
nted unglazed porcelain swivel head on unglazed porcelain shoulder plate,
own human-hair wig, brown glass paperweight eyes, painted upper and lower
shes, ears pierced into lobes, open/closed mouth with four molded teeth,
usseted kid body (repaired with kid) with bisque lower arms, possibly original silk
ess, straw hat, leather shoes stamped with a B
19"
)-01-45
handler Collection, 1962-262.96

he engaging quality of Bru child dolls can be seen immediately in the facial details. Lustrous glass paperweight eyes, chubby cheeks, parted
s with four molded teeth, and delicately painted brows and lashes complete her wistful expression.

means to awaken her interest in and improve her domestic skills. Using the materials then available, she could desig█
cut, sew, and produce exquisite copies of the fashionable gowns worn by her mother to clothe her doll.

The bodies of these dolls could be articulated wood *(poupée bois)* throughout, or they could be gusseted or ungu█
seted kid *(poupée peau)* with leather, wood, or bisque arms. *Harpers Bazaar* observed how they were made in 1884:

> The bodies of the dolls are made in a factory quite unlike those in which the heads and busts are formed. Goo█
> seamstresses are employed, for the sewing-machine here is useless. Everything must be done by hand. The so-calle█
> "French-body," of comparatively recent invention has joints in its limbs, or divisions that do duty as such, and a█
> so durable that little girls have been known to get tired of them. The bodies are variously filled, but horsehair █
> perhaps the best and most popular article for the purpose. Sawdust was once almost exclusively used; but mar█
> of us are old enough to remember the result of "that" process of filling. The doll, growing aged and infirm, an█
> her seams opening could readily be tracked to her hiding-place . . . by the trail she left after her.[2]

Bébés, designed and dressed to look like children between the ages of about six to twelve, were introduced about 187█
and gained in popularity after the Paris Exposition of 1878. They eventually surpassed the adult *poupées* in esteem █
the end of the nineteenth century. Their dolly-faced expression is an idealistic representation of a youngster with pe█
haps a hint of a smile but without any particular personality. Most of these were made of eight-piece composition █
papier-mâché derivative) bodies with ball joints at shoulders, elbows, hips, and knees, strung with elastic that could █
moved and posed. The French *bébés* were also known for their large, expressive, and realistic paperweight glass eye█
Patented by Monsieur Blampoix in 1855, these eyes were so called because the colored irises resembled paperweigh█
in their depth of color and luminosity.[3]

The difference between the adults and children is apparent in the relative size of the body to the head.[4] According █
a patent description by the French firm of Bru, the *poupée* body was seven times the length of the head, while th█
bébé body was five times the length of the head. In addition, the *poupées* have a more sculpted shape with rounde█
derrières, elongated limbs, and sometimes slightly padded bosoms as well as slender oval heads posed on an elonga█
ed throat.

The two-piece swivel head was very popular with the French doll makers between 1860 and 1880 as it allowed f█
flexible positioning. The lower end of the bisque head is ball-shaped and fits into a cup cast into the upper end █
the shoulder plate of the same ceramic material. The two pieces are usually held together by a metal bar which ru█
from the head through the body. The mouths can be either closed or open with or without teeth; the French almo█
always showed mouths closed. The *poupées* as well as the *bébés* had mohair or human hair wigs, although a distin█
guishing feature of the French doll is the cork crown or pate used in the head opening under the wig. The Germa█
doll had a disc of plaster or cardboard instead.

Because German dolls were generally affordable for the middle classes, they became accessible to thousands █
children who could not have purchased the more expensive French counterparts which sold, at a minimum, for twen█
ty dollars by 1919.[5] Very few factories made both doll heads and bodies. Porcelain companies made most of the head█
and supplied more than one doll manufacturer in their own or other countries. The doll manufacturers, in turn█
produced the bodies, assembled the dolls, and added wigs and sometimes clothing. In fact, large numbers of bisqu█
heads were exported and attached to foreign-made bodies later; for example, collectors still consider a German hea█
on a French body, dressed in England, to be an original German doll because they attribute a doll's nationality to th█
country in which the head was made and often marked. In addition to the French firms of Émile Jumeau and Bru Jn█
& Cie, important German makers represented in the Shelburne Museum collection include Simon & Halbig, Arman█
Marseille, Kestner & Co., and Kämmer & Reinhardt.

mile Jumeau opened a new factory at Montreuil-sous-Bois, near Paris, in 1873 where he produced his own bisque eads from 1870 until 1899. However, the Jumeau firm was unusual in that all its activities, including the dressmak-g, were centralized in one location. An official company report published in 1873 stated that "the factory is making oll heads of great perfection and has surpassed in beauty the products previously bought from Saxony. He [Jumeau] as freed us from our former obligation to have foreigners [that is, the Germans] furnish us with porcelain doll heads."[6] 1881 the Jumeau factory became the first French factory to manufacture every component of its dolls.

owever, the Société Française de Fabrication de Bébés et Jouets (S.F.B.J.) was formed in 1899 as a consortium of ajor French companies, including Jumeau and Bru, that produced and marketed its dolls to compete with the grow-g success of the German manufacturers. Yet this endeavor, was ultimately unsuccessful because the quality was not onsistent: the heads were sometimes mass-produced from inferior bisque and could be carelessly modeled. In 1903 *laythings* Magazine wrote, "In dolls Germany rules the world, having wrested supremacy from France."[7] The German sque doll dominated the international market from about 1880 until the 1930s, when the United States had eveloped high-quality composition doll heads and bodies that were unbreakable and became the choice of American arents.

Fig. 124
Poupée
Paris, France
Possibly Jumeau
About 1870
Incised under wig and on each shoulder: 12
Tinted bisque swivel head on unglazed porcelain shoulder plate, light brown human-hair wig, blue threaded-glass paperweight eyes, painted upper and lower lashes, ears pierced into lobes, closed mouth with shading, gusseted kid body with Y stitching in front across lower body, proba-bly original two-piece silk professionally made dress trimmed in ribbons, lace-trimmed hat, leather gloves, cameo pendant, straw basket
h 34 1/2"
20-01-26
Webb Collection, 1952-60

Monthy periodicals devoted to dolls, their clothing, and accessories were published in Paris, beginning in 1863. *La Poupée Modèle*, (The Fashion Doll) was one such magazine. Its publisher, Mme. Peronne, owned a doll shop in the city which was described in the report of the 1867 Paris International Exposition as "the parent of at least two hun-dred establishments of a similar nature which are now scat-tered all over Paris.[8]

Not only was everything provided for the fashionable doll's wardrobe, but additional novelties such as writing paper, scent bottles, playing cards, sewing equipment, folding fans, jewelry, and combs were available for purchase. Some of these accessories are included in the straw basket accompanying this elegant *poupée*. Larger examples, like this one measuring over thirty inches, may have been used in shop windows as a mannequin to promote and advertise the latest fashions.

Fig. 125
Poupée
Paris and Montreuil-sous-Bois,
France
Possibly Bru Jne. & Cie
About 1870-80
Unglazed porcelain swivel head
on unglazed porcelain shoulder
plate, white blonde mohair wig,
painted feathered brows, blue
glass paperweight eyes, painted
upper and lower lashes, ears
pierced into head, soft shaded
peach closed mouth, French kid
body with unjointed legs and
wooden arms ball-jointed at
shoulders, elbows, and wrists,
old clothing, leather gaiter shoes
h 17 ¹/₂"
20-01-47
Chandler Collection, 1961-262.98

Poupée
Chauvière, Paris, France
About 1890
Marked with stamp on chest:
Au Nain Bleu 21 Boulv. Des
Rapugines Chauvière
Unglazed porcelain swivel head
on unglazed porcelain shoulder
plate with raised collar, blonde
mohair wig, blue glass stationary eyes, painted upper and
lower lashes, ears pierced into
head, closed mouth with shading, gusseted kid body with
lower bisque arms, silk and lace
gown
h 17 ¹/₂"
20-01-19
Webb Collection, 1952-60

Poupée
France
About 1870
Unglazed porcelain swivel head
on porcelain shoulder plate,
strawberry blonde human-hair
wig in long braid down back,
blue threaded-glass stationary
eyes, ears pierced into head,
closed mouth, painted wooden
body with swivel-jointed waist
and painted wooden limbs with
mortise-and-tenon joints at
shoulders, elbows, wrists, hips,
knees, and ankles, original silk
dress, cotton pantalets, petticoat, and chemise, and knit
stockings with leather-heeled
boots
h 17"
20-01-79
Gift of Mrs. A. Ruth Whitaker,
1968-109

Beneath their *haute couture*,
these *poupées* exhibit unusual
bodies. The lady at left has a
leather torso and legs combined
with wooden arms ball-jointed
shoulders, elbows, and wrists,
often found on dolls marked B
Jne. & Cie. The original clothing
and underwear on the fashionable doll at right cover a fully
articulated wooden body with
mortise-and-tenon joints. The
stamp on the chest of the doll
center refers to Mlle. Chauvière
who, in 1861, obtained a French
patent for improvements in
making a jointed, stuffed, kid-
body doll. She also appeared in
the Paris directories under
"dolls" from 1863 to 1877 and
was listed as specializing in
jointed *bébés* at her shop au
Nain Bleu, founded in 1836 by
Jean-Baptiste Chauvière, who
was presumably her father.

Fig. 126

Poupée
France
About 1870
Marked inside front shoulder plate: x and ->
Unglazed porcelain swivel head on unglazed porcelain shoulder plate with collar, white mohair wig, painted feathered brows, blue glass eyes, applied ears pierced into lobes, closed mouth with shading, cloth swing-jointed body with leather arms, cotton dress and hat, wool purse
h 22 1/2"
20-01-40
Chandler Collection, 1961-262.85

Poupée
France
About 1870-80
Unglazed porcelain swivel head on unglazed porcelain shoulder plate, blonde mohair wig, painted feathered brows, brown pupilless glass eyes, painted upper and lower lashes, ears pierced into lobes, closed mouth, unjointed kid French body with leather arms, straw hat, dressed in original gown made in 1880
h 10 3/4"
20-01-65
Museum Purchase, 1963-35.2

Poupée
France
About 1870
Incised at top of head in back: F
Unglazed porcelain swivel head on unglazed porcelain shoulder plate, blonde French mohair wig, painted feathered brows, blue glass paperweight eyes, painted upper and lower lashes, ears pierced into head, closed mouth with slight smile, gusseted kid body with lower leather arms, possibly original dress, straw hat
h 16 1/2"
20-01-46
Chandler Collection, 1962-262.97

Poupée
France
About 1870-80
Unglazed porcelain swivel head on unglazed porcelain shoulder plate, white blonde mohair wig, painted feathered brows, blue glass paperweight eyes, painted upper and lower lashes, ears pierced into head, closed mouth, gusseted French kid body, straw hat, redressed by Marta Mengis in old fabric in 1964
h 17"
20-01-16
Webb Collection, 1952-60

Poupée
France
About 1870-80
Incised on back of neck: 4
Unglazed porcelain swivel head on porcelain shoulder plate, blonde mohair wig, painted feathered brows, blue threaded-glass eyes, painted upper and lower lashes, ears pierced into head, closed mouth, French gusseted body with curved leather arms, two-piece walking dress and hat
h 18 3/4"
20-01-17
Webb Collection, 1952-60

All of these fashionable ladies share characteristics of the bisque *poupée*—swivel heads with mohair wigs, pierced ears, glass eyes, and feathered brows. In addition, the doll at left (20-01-40) exhibits an early version of the shoulder plate, with a roll or collar of porcelain around the neck hole.

Fig. 127
Poupée
France
About 1870-80
Unglazed porcelain swivel head on unglazed porcelain shoulder plate, blonde mohair wig, blue glass paperweight eyes, painted upper and lower lashes, closed mouth with shading, kid gusseted body with kid arms, probably original wedding dress
h 12"
20-01-34
Gift of Mrs. E. C. Jacobs, 1959-76

Poupée
France
Body possibly Radiguet & Cordonnier
About 1870-80
Incised on lower back of shoulder plate: R 4 C
Unglazed porcelain swivel head on unglazed porcelain shoulder plate, mohair wig with blue velvet ribbon running through curls, blue glass eyes, no lashes, painted feathered brows, closed mouth, wood articulated and painted body with mortise-and-tenon joints covered in kid at breast and upper arms, hands holding wax flowers, silk and lace wedding gown, probably original underwear
h 18 ½"
20-01-49
Chandler Collection, 1962-262.134

Nurse and Baby
France
About 1870-80
Incised on back of head: 2
Unglazed porcelain swivel head on unglazed porcelain shoulder plate, blonde mohair wig (nurse), blue glass paperweight eyes, painted upper and lower lashes, ears pierced through lobes, closed mouth with shading, unjointed French kid body with bent arms (nurse), wool dress with cape (nurse), crude wooden body and composition arms and legs (baby), long gown (baby), possibly all original
h 15" (nurse), 7" (baby)
20-01-18
Webb Collection, 1952-1960

Poupée
France
About 1870
Unglazed porcelain swivel head on unglazed porcelain shoulder plate, brown mohair wig, blue glass eyes, ears pierced into head, closed mouth with shading, hand-sewn leather kid body with Y seam on lower half of body in front and a three-seam seat in back, short arms, two-piece organdy dress
h 14"
20-01-48
Chandler Collection, 1962-262.99

All but one of these elegant ladies represent brides in either original or very old costumes. Also popular in the 1870s-1890s were French kid-bodied lady dolls commercially dressed as nurses, sometimes in regional costumes, carrying babies.

Fig. 128
Poupée
France
About 1870
Unglazed porcelain swivel head on porcelain shoulder plate, blonde mohair wig, cobalt blue eyes, pierced ears, closed mouth, French kid body with bent arms and gussets at elbows, hips, and knees with stitched toes, cotton underwear
h 16"
20-01-90
Gift of Mrs. Gilbert, 1977-31

Poupée
France
About 1865
Unglazed porcelain swivel head on porcelain shoulder plate, blonde mohair wig, painted feathered brows, stationary cobalt blue eyes, painted upper and lower lashes, pierced ears, closed mouth, French kid gusseted body with lower bisque arms, cotton underwear and stockings, leather shoes
h 15"
20-01-81
Gift of Mrs. Albert E. Walker, 1968-110

These two elegant ladies are dressed in their cotton and lace-trimmed chemises and petticoats to reveal the variations in the French gusseted leather body which could have either gusseted kid (at left) or lower bisque arms (at right).

Fig. 129
Bébé
Montreuil-sous-Bois, France
Jumeau
About 1885-99
Printed decal on back of head: Deposé /Tete Jumeau/Bté S.G.D.G. [*sans guarantie du gouvernement* meaning, "without government guarantee," to indicate that no patent search had been conducted]
Remains of a printed French paper label on back: Au Passage Delo.../JO.../Mon.../R...
Tinted unglazed porcelain shoulder head, missing cork pate, black human-hair wig (replaced), stationary brown glass paperweight eyes, heavily painted brows and upper and lower lashes, ears pierced into head, closed mouth, French composition and wooden ball-jointed body at shoulders, elbows, wrists, hips, and knees
h 26"
20-02-92
Gift of Mrs. Patrick Hill, 1973-8

The eminent Parisian doll-making firm of Jumeau, which introduced the *bébé* dolls in 1876, was a great believer in the power of promotion and advertising and seldom missed an opportunity to extend the market for its products by appealing to the young daughters of richer families. Everything necessary for the retailing of the dolls, including the boxes in which they were to be packaged, was centralized in one location. Between 1880 and 1884 each doll came with a small, sixteen-page booklet extolling the advantages of Jumeau children with their bisque heads, innocent expressions, and composition ball joints:

It is with joy, my kind little lady that I become your baby, for I am sure I will have in you the best and most attentive of little mothers. . . . I am unbreakable, a priceless quality, which I inherit from my father, M. Jumeau, the best of fathers and the most famous of manufacturers. . . . You will be able to comb my hair and wash my face as often as it pleases you. . . . My limbs are so supple and so well articulated that you will be able according to your fancy to have me take any number of different positions. . . . I am beautiful, magnificent, admirable. . . . I am the happiest of babies to have as my little mother a girl so nice as you.[9]

Fig. 130
Bébé
Paris, France
Jumeau
About 1890
Printed decal on back of head: Déposé/Tete Jumeau 7 and in red paint: WXI
Stamped in blue ink on small of back: BeBe Jumeau Bte/.S.G.D.G./ Depose,
Vestiges of paper label on doll's stomach: Boul. des Capucines, 27 Paris
Tinted unglazed porcelain swivel head, blonde mohair French wig, brown paperweight eyes, painted upper and lower lashes, closed painted mouth, composition ball-jointed body with articulated wrists, painted wooden limbs, old clothing, leather shoes marked "Déposé" [meaning registered], kid gloves, leather purse, brass watch and chain, straw hat
h 17 3/4"
20-01-67
Gift of Mrs. William C. Morris, 1963-172

Bébé
Probably France
About 1890
Tinted unglazed porcelain swivel head, blonde mohair wig, brown glass sleep eyes, heavily painted brows and upper and lower lashes, septum between nostrils very pronounced, small open mouth with two square teeth, dimple in chin, composition body with ball joints at shoulders and unjointed wrists, internal talking box, cotton and rayon dress, straw hat with velvet flowers and ostrich feather, soles of French leather shoes stamped C. M. and 6.
h 18"
20-01-33
Gift of Mrs. C. Francis Beatty, 1958-261

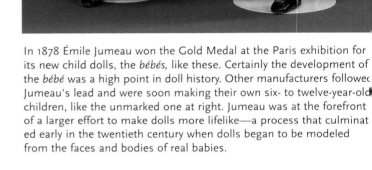

In 1878 Émile Jumeau won the Gold Medal at the Paris exhibition for its new child dolls, the *bébés*, like these. Certainly the development of the *bébé* was a high point in doll history. Other manufacturers followed Jumeau's lead and were soon making their own six- to twelve-year-old children, like the unmarked one at right. Jumeau was at the forefront of a larger effort to make dolls more lifelike—a process that culminated early in the twentieth century when dolls began to be modeled from the faces and bodies of real babies.

Fig. 131
Bébé
Probably France
About 1890
Tinted unglazed porcelain shoulder head, blond mohair wig, blue glass paperweight eyes, painted upper and lower lashes, pierced ears, open mouth with teeth, dimple in chin, French-type child's kid body with gussets at elbows, hips, and knees, tinted unglazed porcelain lower arms, cotton dress, apron, and socks
h 23"
20-01-87
Gift of Miss Marjorie Fisher, 1977-1

Bébé
Paris, France
Rabery & Delphieu
About 1879
Stamped into back of doll's neck: RoD
Tinted unglazed porcelain on unglazed porcelain shoulder plate, short reddish blonde mohair wig, stationary brown glass paperweight eyes, painted upper and lower lashes, ears pierced into lobes, closed mouth, ball-jointed French composition body with straight wrists, turned-wood upper limbs, redressed in old cotton jumper, blouse petticoat, and pantalets, mesh socks, new leather shoes
h 16"
20-01-94
Gift of Dr. and Mrs. M. C. Twitchell, 1981-70

The *bébé* on the left is distinguished by her open mouth with teeth. The child on the right is marked by the Paris firm of Rabery & Delphieu, which advertised jointed dolls with wooden bodies that were sold either dressed or undressed in 1881.[10]

Fig. 132
Bébé
Paris and Montreuil-sous-Bois, France
Bru Jne. & Cie
About 1880
Incised on shoulder: Bru Jne
Paper label on front of chest: Bru
Tinted unglazed porcelain swivel head on
unglazed porcelain shoulder plate, light
brown human-hair wig, ears pierced into
lobes, brown glass paperweight eyes, painted upper and lower lashes, closed mouth
with tongue tip showing, kid gusseted body
with bisque lower arms, redressed by Marta
Mengis in 1961 in old silk dress with lace
and velvet trim
h 19 3/4"
20-01-27
Gift of Miss Eleanor Whitmer, 1953-1006

Bébé
Paris and Montreuil-sous-Bois, France
Probably Bru Jne. & Cie
About 1880
Tinted unglazed porcelain swivel head on
unglazed porcelain shoulder plate, brown
human-hair wig, brown glass paperweight
eyes, painted upper and lower lashes, ears
pierced into lobes, open/closed mouth with
four molded teeth, kid gusseted body
(repaired with kid) with bisque lower arms,
possibly original silk dress, leather shoes
stamped with a B
h 19"
20-01-45
Chandler Collection, 1962-262.96

Bébé
Paris and   Montreuil-sous-Bois, France
Bru Jne. & Cie
About 1883-90
Incised on shoulder plate: Bru Jne 8
Incised on head: Bru Jne 8
Stamped on shoe: Bru Jne., Paris, 8
Tinted unglazed porcelain swivel head on
unglazed porcelain shoulder plate, light
brown human-hair wig, brown glass paperweight eyes, painted upper and lower lashes,
ears pierced into lobes, closed mouth with
tongue tip showing, kid body with bisque
lower arms and wooden lower legs, wire hip
joints in leather, green faded to gold silk
gown
h 22"
20-01-25
Webb Collection, 1952-60

In 1866 Leon Casimir Bru founded the French firm Bru Jne. & Cie ("Bru the Younger and Company,") originally to assemble *poupées* and dress them in exclusive costumes, many for export to America.[11] However, the company went on to produce dolls of the latest models and inventions and is credited with at least twenty-five patents throughout its history. Bru dolls are visible proof that the company was preeminent in the field of doll making. These *bébés* are dressed in the height of style in silk, satin, velvet, or brocade garments with trim-mings of shimmering ribbons, delicate lace, and elegant chapeau. Even leather boots and shoes made for Bru dolls are stamped with the maker's name inside an oval.

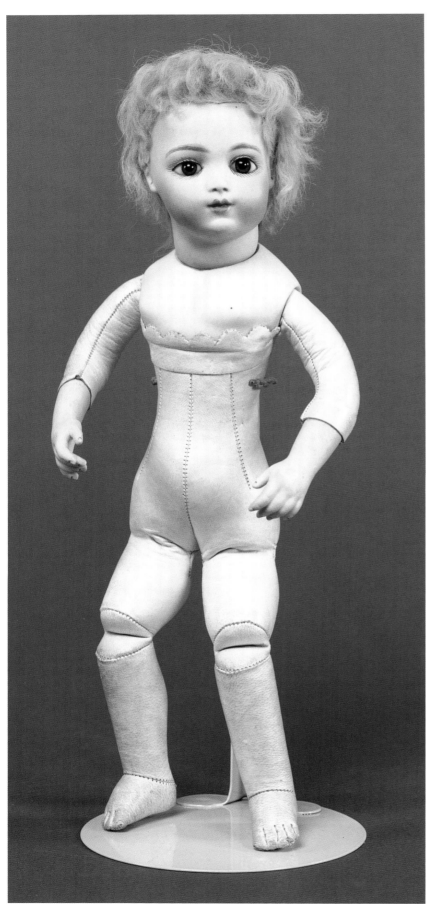

Fig. 133
Bébé
Paris and Montreuil-sous-Bois, France
Bru Jne. & Cie
About 1880
Stamped on shoulder: Bru Jne 2
Stamped on back of head under hair: Bru Jne 2
Tinted unglazed porcelain swivel head on unglazed porcelain shoulder plate, skin wig, brown glass paperweight eyes, painted upper and lower lashes, ears pierced into lobes, closed mouth, gusseted kid body with lower bisque arms
h 13"
20-01-30
Gift of Miss Mabel Earl, 1955-572

Bru *bébés* could be purchased naked, partly dressed in chemise and drawers, or fully clothed. The most sought-after of all the *bébé* Brus are those with kid bodies like this one. She has a molded-bisque shoulder plate with bosom, a strip of kid scalloped on the upper side glued over the joint and around the body, and lower bisque arms with beautifully shaped hands and flesh-tinted knuckles. Her firmly padded torso with rounded belly has gussets between the buttocks and thigh and at the knees to allow the legs to bend.

As the pioneer founder of the doll
industry in the Waltershausen area in
1816, J. D. Kestner is the most important name in the history of German doll
production there. In 1860 his heirs continued the business and established a
new porcelain factory at Ohrdruf, where
the company was the first to manufacture the complete doll—that is, both

heads and bodies of cloth and leather.
They produced bisque lady dolls that
were a direct descendent of the French
Parisiennes, modeled after the aristocratic and captivating society ladies
drawn by American illustrator Charles
Gibson, first for *Life Magazine* of 1890
and later for *Collier's Weekly*.

This tall, willowy, and haughtily lovely
young lady of fashion was modeled
after Gibson's own wife. Characterized
by upswept hairdo, arched eyebrows,
upturned nose, pointy chin, and slender
throat, the doll is dressed in Edwardian
clothing with a high-collared blouse, a
long sweeping skirt, and an enormous
hat. The patrician "Gibson Girl" doll
was widely imported into America by
George Borgfeldt Corporation in New
York, in business from about 1882 to
1925. His company imported and distributed the finest dolls manufactured
abroad.

In an 1888 announcement Kestner & Co. advertised
bisque doll heads. "They are partly straight positioned
on the shoulders, partly slightly sidewards directed
and they are quite impressive with their stationary or
movable glass eyes, their inserted teeth and their
magnificent mohair wigs."[12]

Fig. 136
Lady
Gräfenhain, Thuringia, Germany
Simon & Halbig (head)
Successors of Jules Steiner, France (body)
About 1906-8
Incised on head: S &H
Red ink oval stamp on head below incising: Wimperrn Gesetzl.
Geschutzt
Stamped in clay in center of red ink stamp: 05 and 7
Decal on back of body: E./D.B./Paris/D.P
Tinted unglazed porcelain swivel head, brown mohair wig, blue glass
sleep eyes, painted lower lashes with fur upper lashes, ears pierced
into lobes with cameo earrings, open mouth with four inset porcelain
teeth, jointed papier-mâché body with molded bosom and small waist,
unjointed wrists, silk dress, linen pantalets and slim slip, cotton petticoat
h 19 ³/₄"
20-01-35
Gift of Mrs. S. Bayard Colgate, 1959-181.1

Lady
Gräfenhain, Thuringia, Germany
Simon & Halbig (head)
About 1910
Incised on head: S &H/DEP/8/Germany
Red oval stamp on neck below incising: Wimper
Tinted unglazed porcelain swivel head, blonde mohair wig, molded
painted brows, blue glass sleep eyes, fur upper eyelashes, ears pierced
into lobes, open mouth with four inset porcelain teeth, composition ball-
jointed body with molded bosom and small waist, unjointed wrists and
fingers molded together, cotton corset, chemise, petticoat, and pantalets
h 22 ³/₄"
20-01-32
Gift of Miss Eleanore Schnepf, 1957-545.2

The German factories were noted for innovation. They developed
sleeping eyes with many different kinds of movement, open
mouths with inset or molded teeth, voice boxes of various types,
and real fur eyelashes *(wimpern)* exhibited by these two similar
bisque heads made by Simon & Halbig.

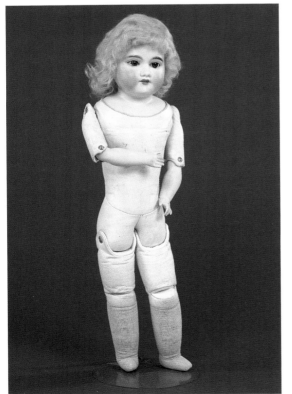

Fig. 137
Girl
Köppelsdorf, Thuringia, Germany
Armand Marseille (head)
Sarah Robinson (body)
About 1895
Incised on back: Floradora/A-3-M/Made in Germany
Tinted unglazed porcelain shoulder plate, replaced blonde mohair wig, brown
glass sleep eyes, painted brows and upper and lower lashes, open mouth with
teeth, leather body with Robinson-type joints at elbows and hips, gusset at knee,
lower cloth legs, lower bisque arms
h 19 ¹/₂"
20-01-77
Gift of Mrs. Robert G. Stauffer, 1971-37

Russian-born Armand Marseille established a factory at Köppelsdorf, Germany, in
1892 and became the most prolific manufacturer of bisque doll heads in the world
until about 1925.

"Floradora" was the trademark registered by Borgfeldt in Germany for dolls with
kid bodies and bisque heads made by Armand Marseille from about 1901 to 1909
and exported primarily to America. These sweet dolly faces appealed to the public
because of their large pretty eyes and gentle expressions. Floradora shoulder head
were combined with kid bodies, usually reserved for finer dolls such as this one
patented by Sarah Robinson of Chicago, Illinois, in 1883. It features moveable
hinged joints at the elbows and thighs and fastened with buttons or rivets to
prevent them from cutting the fabric.

Fig. 138
Girl
Köppelsdorf, Thuringia, Germany
Armand Marseille
About 1912
Incised on back of head: Made in Germany/Armand
Marseille/390/DRGM 246/1/A9M
Tinted unglazed porcelain socket head, original brown wig with bow
still tied in hair, brown glass sleep eyes, inserted mohair lashes,
open mouth with teeth, German composition ball-jointed body at
shoulders, elbows, wrist, hips, and shoulders, homemade original
clothing including underwear, socks, and high-top leather boots
h 24"
20-01-76
Gift of Mrs. Eliza Kemp Lunger, 1971-46

Girl
Köppelsdorf, Thuringia, Germany
Armand Marseille
About 1890
Incised on back of head: Germany/390/A7M
Tinted unglazed porcelain socket head, mohair wig, blue glass sleep
eyes, inserted mohair lashes, open mouth with teeth, German com-
position ball-jointed body at knees and elbows, original cotton che-
mise
h 23"
20-01-84
Museum Collection, 2004-1

The most popular model for export was Armand Marseille's dolly
face mold #390 with its glass sleep eyes, open mouth with teeth,
and mohair wig with inserted lashes. Placed on ball-jointed composition bodies, these socket heads and limbs could be posed in many
positions. These two dolls also exhibit their original clothing. The
girl at left has her homemade dress and hat, while the one at right
wears a factory-made chemise. The underwear the dolls wore is generally a faithful miniature copy of what stylish women chose, made

from the same materials and fashioned in the same styles.
Chemises such as the one at right were usually knee-length and
straight-cut with the fullness gathered or arranged in neat tucks into
a yoke at the neck. These high-cut models, used for day-wear under
clothes, generally featured a short, buttoned opening at the center
front, as shown here.

Fig. 139
Boy
Waltershausen, Thuringia, Germany
Simon & Halbig (head)
Heinrich Handwerck (body)
About 1900
Incised on back of head: 182
Stamped on body at waist: Heinrich Handwerck
Tinted unglazed porcelain swivel head, reddish mohair wig, brown glass sleep eyes
with upper and lower mohair lashes, open mouth with four teeth, composition
ball-jointed body, wool suit made by donor's grandfather's tailor with top hat
marked, "Truly Warner Designer, New York, Broadway," leather shoes
h 22"
20-01-31
Gift of Miss Eleanor Schnepf, 1957-545.1

In 1888, Heinrich Handwerck advertised ball-jointed doll bodies made of composition for which he won the highest award in the 1893 world exhibition at Chicago.
He engaged Simon & Halbig in Gräfenhain, Thuringia, to pour bisque heads for
him after his own designs. As many of the completed dolls were exported to
America dressed primarily in underwear, it is not surprising that, according to the
donor, this dashing young boy was costumed in his dress suit after his arrival in
the United States.

Fig. 140
Girl
Gräfenhain, Thuringia, Germany
Possibly Simon & Halbig
About 1910
Tinted bisque shoulder head, blonde mohair
wig, blue glass eyes, painted eyebrows and
upper and lower lashes, ears pierced into
head, closed mouth, polished cotton body
with swing joints at shoulders and hips,
lower unglazed limbs with bare feet and
molded toes, velvet dress and hat, lace
apron, cotton slip
h 8"
20-01-86
Gift of Mrs. Eric Stone, 1975-57

Girl
Gräfenhain, Thuringia, Germany
Simon & Halbig
About 1900
Incised on back of shoulder: S & H 1160/
Little Women Dolls
Tinted unglazed porcelain shoulder head,
blonde mohair wig in long pencil curls ("little woman" type), brown pupilless glass
eyes, painted upper and lower lashes, closed
mouth, cloth swing-jointed body with lower
unglazed porcelain limbs, painted three-
strap shoes and blue garter, original cotton
chemise, petticoat, and pantalets
h 8 ½"
20-01-01
Webb Collection, 1952-60

The Simon & Halbig porcelain factory
opened in 1869 and produced some of the
finest bisque doll heads in terms of their
exquisite painting and the variety and dis-
tinctiveness of their models. Even during the
long period of domination of the dolly-faced
doll, many of the Simon & Halbig designs
represented individuality to convey a sense
of personality rather than an idealized childlike expression.

Simon & Halbig supplied numerous doll factories with either their own inventory heads
or designs commissioned by other doll manufacturers including Kämmer & Reinhardt
(founded in 1885) which actually purchased
the Simon & Halbig factory in 1920.

wiss Girl
öppelsdorf, Thuringia, Germany
rmand Marseille
bout 1900
cised on back of neck: A. M./390
nted unglazed porcelain socket head,
own mohair wig, brown glass sleep eyes,
ainted upper and lower lashes, open
outh with teeth, composition body ball-
inted at shoulders, elbows, wrist, hips, and
ees, wool skirt, velvet vest with embroi-
ered beads, cotton shirt, hat with lace trim,
ather shoes with metal buckles
9"
)-01-59
ebb Collection, 1952-60

frican American Girl
räfenhain, Thuringia, Germany
ossibly Simon & Halbig
bout 1900
cised on back of head: 30-5/Dep/th
nted unglazed porcelain socket head, black
er wig, brown glass eyes, open mouth
th four teeth, composition stick ball-joint-
l body, cotton dress with cotton pantalets,
tticoat with ruffle, wool hat with silk rib-
n and ostrich feather
18"
)-01-23
ebb Collection, 1952-60

Swiss Girl
Waltershausen, Thuringia, Germany
Kämmer & Reinhardt
About 1895
Incised on back of head: Simon & Halbig/K*R
Tinted unglazed porcelain socket head,
blonde mohair wig, blue glass sleep eyes,
painted upper and lower lashes, open
mouth with teeth, five-piece jointed composition body, cotton dress, apron, and hat,
velvet vest, molded two strap shoes and
heels, celluloid baby
h 9"
20-01-52
Webb Collection, 1952-60

Scottish Girl
Germany
About 1900
Tinted unglazed porcelain head, brown
mohair wig, blue glass sleep eyes, painted
upper and lower lashes, open mouth with
four teeth, five-piece jointed composition
body with straight legs, wool tartan skirt and
socks, velvet jacket and cap with metal buck-
le, silk blouse, lace scarf, tag under skirt,
almost gone, reads in part, "d-& co./wt"
h 12"
20-01-53
Webb Collection, 1952-60

Polish Girl
Köppelsdorf, Thuringia, Germany
Armand Marseille
About 1900
Incised on back of neck: AM
Tinted unglazed porcelain socket head, no
wig, cotton embroidered cap, brown glass
stationary eyes, painted upper and lower
lashes, open mouth with teeth, five-piece
jointed sawdust composition body, wool
dress
h 11"
20-01-51
Webb Collection, 1952-1960

These German dolly-faced girls have open
mouths with teeth and jointed composition
bodies. Unlike other children dressed in
high fashion clothes, these represent different nationalities either through their original
ethnic costumes—Swiss, Polish, or
Scottish—or tinted complexion (African
American).

Fig. 142
Boy
Licht and Sonneberg, Thuringia, Germany
Gebrüder Heubach
About 1910
Incised on back: sun mark
Tinted unglazed porcelain shoulder head, brown flocked hair,
intaglio (hollow) eyes, closed mouth, cloth body with composition
lower arms and swing-jointed legs, polished cotton pants, cotton
shirt
h 11"
20-01-63
Webb Collection, 1952-60

Girl
Waltershausen, Thuringia, Germany
Kämmer & Reinhardt
1886-95
Incised on back of head: K * R / 114
Tinted unglazed porcelain socket head, blonde mohair wig, painted
brown eyes, five-piece jointed composition body with molded shoes,
original linen apron and checked dress
h 7 1/2"
20-01-61
Webb Collection, 1952-60

Girl "Marie"
Waltershausen, Thuringia, Germany
Kämmer & Reinhardt
1909
Incised on back of head: K*R/101
Tinted unglazed porcelain socket head, brown mohair wig, painted
eyes, painted mouth, five-piece composition body jointed at shoulders and hips with molded boots, original cotton dress
h 8"
20-01-21
Webb Collection, 1952-60

While the makers in France continued to create dolly-faced dolls of
an idealized femininity and beauty, German companies of the late
nineteenth century turned their attention to a novel idea—creating
dolls with a variety of emotions and personalities. The Kämmer &
Reinhardt doll factory was founded in 1885, but its most famous
designs were produced in 1909 when they were the first to register
"Character Dolls" as a trade name. Using heads poured by the prestigious Simon & Halbig porcelain factory after Kämmer & Reinhardt
designs, the firm produced faces that reflected the full range of children's moods. "Marie," for example, has pouty lips and painted
incised eyes, an expression for which Kämmer & Reinhardt was
known, and wears her original provincial costume.

Starting in 1910, the Heubach brothers made bisque head baby, toddler, and child character dolls, like this boy, notable for their hollow
(intaglio) eyes—with the iris and pupil deeply situated in the mold
and then painted. The distinctive concave surface of the eyes gives
them a natural expression.

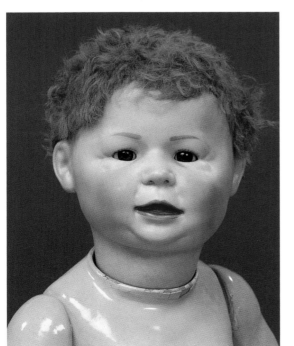

Fig. 143
Character Toddler
Gräfenhain, Thuringia, Germany
Simon & Halbig
About 1915
Incised on back of head: 1428
Tinted unglazed porcelain socket head, red blonde skin wig, stationary blue glass
eyes, painted upper lashes, large open/closed mouth, five-piece jointed bent-limb
composition baby body
h 23"
20-02-93
Gift of Mrs. Patrick Hill, 1973-8

This engaging baby face with pudgy features, large open mouth with tongue, and
striking red animal skin wig exemplifies the appealing qualities of the German
character doll.

Fig. 144

"Bye-Lo" Baby
Germany
Grace Storey Putnam
1923
Incised on back of neck: Copr by/Grace S
Putnam/made in Germany
Tinted unglazed porcelain flange head,
painted molded hair, glass sleep eyes, closed
mouth, frog-type cloth body with celluloid
hands, cotton slip
16"
Museum Collection, 2004-4

Baby "Grete"
Sonneberg, Germany
Porzellanfabrik Mengersgereuth
About 1929
Incised on neck: P.M///Grete 3/0
Tinted unglazed porcelain, blonde mohair
wig, brown glass sleep eyes, open mouth
with teeth, five-piece composition bent limb
German baby body, cotton dress, diaper,
slip, and bonnet
11"
20-01-72
Gift of Miss Fannie Pierce, 1967-84

"Bye- Lo" Baby
Germany
Grace Storey Putnam
1923
Incised on back of neck: copyright 1923
by/Grace S. Putnam/made in Germany
Tinted unglazed porcelain flange head,
molded painted hair, brown glass sleep eyes,
closed mouth, frog-type cotton body with
cardboard-covered crier in center back
stamped in black, "MFG'D by THE ART
METAL WORKS/NEWARK, N. J., Pat pend-
ing," plaster-filled celluloid hands, cotton
dress
h 14 1/4"
20-01-69
Gift of Miss Nancy Coy, 1965-111

"My Dream Baby" Infant
Köppelsdorf, Thuringia, Germany
Armand Marseille
About 1924
Incised on back of neck:
Germany///431/2k///AM
Tinted unglazed porcelain socket head,
painted hair, blue glass sleep eyes, closed
mouth, five-piece bent limb composition
baby body, internal voice box
h 12 1/2"
Museum Collection, 2004-3

The popularity of baby dolls peaked during
the 1920s. Former Mills College art teacher
Grace Storey Putnam of Oakland, California,
sculpted a life-size wax model of a three-day-
old infant with folds of fat and half-open
eyes. To supply the increasing demand for
character dolls with realistic features,
German manufacturers such as A.W. Fr.
Kister and C.F. Kling & Co. mass-produced
Putnam's bisque "bye-lo" baby, and George
Borgfeldt distributed the doll in the United
States.[13] Bye-lo babies share top billing with
Barbie and Shirley Temple as the biggest
money-making dolls of all time. Other
German companies followed suit with their
named versions such as "My Dream Baby"
and "Grete," shown here. These infant heads
are attached to one-piece frog-shaped cotton
bodies or bent-limb composition bodies
appropriate to a newborn.

Parian-Type Dolls

Parian ware is an unglazed, untinted biscuit porcelain resembling a fine-grained white marble, which displays a certain similarity to the marble used for ancient Greek statuary from the island of Paros, hence the name Parian. Invented in Stoke-on-Trent, England, by William Copeland in 1848, it is characterized by its permeability to light and its resulting semitranslucent surface. Because of the high cost required to achieve this effect, parian ware was considered almost an art medium and was used primarily to manufacture figurines and vases.

After about 1850, the German doll manufacturers attempted to develop a similar parian formula, yet the result did not attain the fineness and transparency of the original English material. The German version of this white bisque was less expensive and more easily worked; nonetheless the manufacturers used the misleading term "parian" dolls and doll heads in advertisements during the middle of the nineteenth century. To complicate matters further, true bisque doll heads with matte, flesh-tinted porcelain were produced about 1870. The shading was so fine and pale that it is often difficult to distinguish between so-called German parian and bisque. Both materials were employed for similarly molded doll heads produced simultaneously, often making an accurate identification almost impossible.

For this reason, the term "parian-type" applies to dolls in the Shelburne Museum collection with both pure white or pale-tinted complexions that are highly decorated. They are characterized by elaborately modeled blond hair often

continued on next page

g. 145
.dy
·äfenroda, Thuringia, Germany
tributed to Dornheim, Koch & Fischer
out 1870
ecorated parian-type porcelain shoulder head with pierced ears and earrings,
olded blonde hair with molded pink bow and real brown feather, center part with
o puffs of short curls at top pulled to back above ears into rolls and curls, paint-
blue eyes with highlights, painted mouth with darker line between lips, square
ff of lace molded around neck with gold beads, cloth swing-jointed body and
wer leather arms, redressed by Mrs. George Chandler in silk walking dress deco-
ted with coral beads made from antique fabric and brass chain-link pocket
urse) attached to jacket
17 1/4"
·-06-53
andler Collection, 1962-262.122

is rare, highly embellished lady exhibits all the distinguishing features of the ultimate decorated parian-type doll—elaborately molded hair-
adorned with a glazed, ceramic bow and a real feather, pierced ears and faux pearl and lapis drop earrings and a square-necked guimpe,
bodice, worn under a low-necked dress trimmed with molded gold beads and a ruffle.

embellished with flowers, feathers, or ribbons in many colors and sometimes with the addition of rich metallic luster and gold paint, pierced ears with earrings, blue eyes with eyelid strokes, red dots in the corners of the eyes, and rosy cheeks. Light brown (so-called "café-au-lait") or black hair, molded shoulder plate decorations with applied collars, ruffs and jewelry, inserted glass eyes, and swivel heads are the rare exceptions. Later collectors have named several of the distinctive hairstyles on these parian-type dolls after well-known personalities such as Empress Eugénie of France, the German Kaiserin Augusta, and Queen Louise of Prussia or after such fictional characters as Alice in Wonderland. Dolls depicting boys and men with distinct short hairstyles are still rare.

These dolls can have cloth homemade or manufactured bodies with bisque, china, or kid lower arms. Following Parisian fashion, the late 1860s and early 1870s marked a period of great interest in the newest styles. Parian-type dolls dressed in the most elaborate au courant costumes were clearly made for display rather than play and thus marketed to adults rather than children. Although a number of successful manufacturers were operating in Thuringia, Germany, very few marked their products prior to 1860, and so factory production cannot be readily identified. However, based on Krombholz's recent research, it is possible to compare unmarked dolls with newly discovered printed sample books as well as with excavated fragments and molds found on the sites of old established porcelain factories.[1] Her identification of distinctive modeling and painting characteristics—including the shape of the face; color and highlight placement of the irises; and shape and color of the eyebrows and mouth—make it possible to attribute virtually all of the parian-type dolls in the Shelburne Museum collection to Alt, Beck & Gottschalck (Nauendorf, Thuringia), Conta & Böhme (Pössneck, Thuringia), Dornheim, Koch & Fischer (Gräfenroda, Thuringia), A.W. Fr. Kister (Scheibe-Alsbach, Thuringia), C.F. Kling & Co. (Ohrdruf, Thuringia), Kestner & Co. (Ohrdruf, Thuringia), Simon & Halbig Gräfenhain, Thuringia), or Hertwig & Co. (Katzhütte, Thuringia).

Fig. 146
Lady
Gräfenroda, Thuringia, Germany
Attributed to Dornheim, Koch & Fischer
About 1860-70
Parian-type shoulder head, molded painted blonde hair swept up on sides with cascade of curls on forehead then folded in back and decorated with two braids exposing ears, unpainted square molded yoke, painted blue eyes that look threaded, painted upper and lower lashes, cloth swing-jointed body with leather arms, embroidered cotton dress
h 15"
20-06-04
Webb Collection, 1952-60

Lady
Gräfenroda, Thuringia, Germany
Attributed to Dornheim, Koch & Fischer
About 1875
Parian-type shoulder head, molded shoulder plate including blouse front with blue trimming and pink striped bow at neck, molded coffee-colored hair with center part and two poufs on top, swept up on sides and gathered into a mass of curls in back, painted blue eyes with two highlights, pierced ears with celadon-colored bead earring, cloth body with leather upper arms and bisque legs, silk dress made from "English costumes 1867"
h 18"
20-06-5
Chandler Collection, 1962-262.119

Based on their skin tone, there is no question that these two ladies are made of untinted bisque. Both are attributed to the porcelain factory of Dornheim, Koch & Fischer due to the tight molded curls on the left and the distinctive shoulder plate decoration on the right.

Fig. 147

Lady
Gräfenroda, Thuringia, Germany
Attributed to Dornheim, Koch & Fischer
About 1860-70
Incised on underside of front shoulder plate: 55
Written in black under back: 55
Decorated parian-type shoulder head, molded painted blonde hair
with center part swept away from the face with wings on the side,
snood in back, and roll of hair falling down neck into a pageboy,
painted blue eyes with white highlights, yoke with molded and painted collar, old cloth swing-jointed body with leather arms, gingham
dress
h 18 ¹/₄"
20-06-34
Chandler Collection, 1962-262.103

Gentleman
Gräfenroda, Thuringia, Germany
Attributed to Dornheim, Koch & Fischer
About 1875
Written on upper left arm in brown ink script: MP over 15
Parian-type shoulder head, molded coffee-colored hair with center
part brushed back behind ears into a page boy, painted blue eyes
with white highlights, circle-dot nose, molded collar with gold- and
blue-striped bow tie, old cloth swing-jointed body with lower
leather arms
h 15 ¹/₂"
20-06-32
Chandler Collection, 1962-262.101

The distinctive hairstyles define the gender of each of these male
and female dolls. However, both of them share the same shoulder
plate, which is molded to depict a shirt collar and blue-and-white-
striped tie, glazed and trimmed with gilding. This is an identified
model produced by Dornheim, Koch & Fischer.[2]

Fig. 148
Girl
Gräfenroda, Thuringia,
Germany
Attributed to Dornheim,
Koch & Fischer
About 1860-70
Decorated parian-type
shoulder head, molded
painted café-au-lait hair
swept up away from face
exposing ears with mold-
ed blue band trimmed in
gold around head tied into
bow leaving waves in
back, painted blue eyes
with highlights, new cloth
body (later than head)
with old china limbs with pink heeled boots,
redressed by Mrs. F. C. Jeffries in old cotton sprigged
dress trimmed in lace
h 13"
20-06-56
Chandler Collection, 1962-262.125

Girl
Ohrdruf, Thuringia, Germany
Attributed to C.F. Kling & Co.
About 1860-70
Incised inside back of shoulder plate: 2
Decorated parian-type shoulder head, molded painted
blonde hair swept up high on sides with two curls on
forehead in pompadour style with molded black comb
on head, scalloped neckline with (applied) lace ruching over blue band with fine burgundy detailing, painted blue eyes, old cloth swing-jointed body with lower
unglazed porcelain arms, legs, and blue boots with
heels, redressed by Mrs. George Chandler in silk and
cotton costume
h 14"
20-06-47
Chandler Collection, 1962-262.116

Despite their small size, these young girls exhibit the
same elaborate coiffures and hair accessories as the
larger parian-type ladies. The shoulder head on the
right has a molded scalloped neckline with applied
lace ruching to enhance her costume and the downturned mouth associated with the Kling factory.[3]

Fig. 149
Girl
Nauendorf, Thuringia, Germany
Attributed to Alt, Beck & Gottschalck
About 1880
Decorated parian-type shoulder head, molded painted blonde hair swept up and away
from face exposing ears and held back with
molded black band leaving hair falling in
soft curls and waves, painted blue outlined
eyes, old cloth swing-jointed body with lower
unglazed porcelain arms, copper luster with
gold china boots, detailed painted stockings,
batiste clothing, talking box in torso
h 21"
20-06-03
Webb Collection, 1952-60

Girl
Ohrdruf, Thuringia, Germany
Attributed to C.F. Kling & Co.
About 1860-70
Decorated parian-type shoulder head with
pierced ears and slightly turned head, molded painted blonde hair in ringlets around
face and swept back into cascade of curls
held with molded blue luster tied ribbon,
painted blue eyes outlined in black, new
cloth swing-jointed body with leather arms,
redressed in silk gown by Mrs. George
Chandler
h 21 1/4"
20-06-37
Chandler Collection, 1962-262.106

Girl
Nauendorf, Thuringia, Germany
Attributed to Alt, Beck & Gottschalck
About 1860-70
Incised and painted in red on inside of
shoulder plate: 10 8
Decorated parian-type shoulder head with
pierced ears and glass drop earrings, molded painted blonde hair with center part
pulled back from face and braids tied in
molded blue bow over wavy hair falling to
neck, glass eyes with painted upper and
lower lashes, old cloth swing-jointed body
with leather lower arms, cotton chemise,
petticoat, and lace-trimmed pantalets
h 18 1/2"
20-06-23
Chandler Collection, 1962-262.83

These three young girls are characterized by round faces and short necks. The doll at left has
unique copper and gold luster boots as well as a nonfunctioning talking box in the middle of
her torso. The one in the middle is remarkable for her molded head looking slightly to her
left, found only on Kling models, and the corners of her mouth are downturned, which is
also typical of this factory's painting.[4] The doll at right has unusual glass eyes.

Fig. 150
Girl
Nauendorf, Thuringia, Germany
Attributed to Alt, Beck & Gottschalck
About 1875
Parian-type shoulder head, molded painted
blonde hair swept back from face with molded black band on top ("Alice" style), painted
blue eyes, leather body swing-jointed at
shoulders, hips, and knees with green
leather bands at knees, stitched triangular
feet, cotton corset laced in front and back
10 3/4"
20-01-96
Gift of Jeanne Ericson, 1986-21.6

Girl
Nauendorf, Thuringia, Germany
Attributed to Alt, Beck & Gottschalck
About 1860-70
Parian-type shoulder head, molded painted
light brown hair with center part and two
curls at temples and molded band over head
to hold back long sausage curls, painted
blue eyes, old cloth swing-jointed body,
lower unglazed porcelain limbs with flat feet
and black painted shoes, costume made in
1965 of silk fabric and lace
h 10"
20-06-59
Gift of Mr. Richmond W. Wight, 1962-175.2

Girl
Nauendorf, Thuringia, Germany
Attributed to Alt, Beck & Gottschalck
About 1860-70
Parian-type shoulder head, molded painted
pale blonde hair with center part and flat
across head then pulled back into sausage
curls ("flat-top" style), painted blue eyes,
closed mouth with white separation, old
cloth swing-jointed body with unglazed
porcelain lower limbs, glazed black shoes
with flat soles, dotted-swiss cotton dress,
straw hat
h 9 1/4"
20-06-21
Chandler Collection, 1962-262.81

The model for the very popular doll on the left was Alice from Lewis Carroll's fairy tale book
Alice in Wonderland (1865). Produced by several companies, including Kister, Kling, and Alt,
Beck & Gottschalck, the Alice at left has her original kid body with unusual green leather
bands at the knees and stitched triangular feet and wears a corset that laces up both front
and back. All three girls exhibit the chubby cheeks associated with the Alt, Beck &
Gottschalck porcelain factory.[5]

Fig. 151
Boy
Gräfenroda, Thuringia, Germany
Attributed to Dornheim, Koch & Fischer
About 1860-70
Parian-type shoulder head, molded painted cafe-au-lait hair with
side part swept up and over top of head, painted blue eyes with
white highlights, unjointed cloth body with small china arms, origi-
nal dark grape wool suit, cotton underclothes
h 17"
20-06-18
Gift of Mr. Joseph Barrell, 1951-15

This rare male doll with café-au-lait-colored hair and fine brushstrokes at the forehead is even more remarkable for his striking
original costume. His complete outfit consists of cotton ribbed
drawers and undershirt with mother-of-pearl buttons; wool
trousers, vest, and pants; a linen shirt with a detachable collar;
woven braces; and a silk cravat. He is even equipped with additional accessories including a linen handkerchief, brass buttons
stamped "Derby," and a pocket watch with fob. His upper arms are
presumably left unstuffed to allow for maximum flexibility when
dressing or undressing. Is he the nineteenth-century equivalent of
the twentieth-century Ken doll?

Girl
Nauendorf, Thuringia, Germany
Attributed to Alt, Beck & Gottschalck
About 1860-70
Decorated parian-type shoulder head with
pierced ears and jet teardrop-shaped earrings, molded painted blonde hair with
molded blue band in front, blue glass eyes
with painted upper and lower lashes, homemade cloth swing-jointed body with leather
arms, green silk dress, cotton chemise and
pantalets
h 16 3/4"
20-06-10
Webb Collection, 1952-60

Lady
Ohrdruf, Thuringia, Germany
Attributed to C.F. Kling & Co.
About 1880
Parian-type shoulder head with pierced ears
and pearl earrings, molded painted blonde
hair with center part and ringlets around
face exposing ears and pulled to braided circle on top with long curls gathered together
at center in back, blue glass eyes, painted
upper and lower lashes, manufactured cloth
swing-jointed body with unglazed bisque
arms, silk and velvet gown with leather
shoes, cotton underwear
h 22"
20-06-07
Webb Collection, 1952-60

All three of these blonde parian-type shoulder heads with pierced ears and jewelry are distinguished by their inset blue glass eyes—much rarer than painted features. The chubby cheeks
and lips painted a soft shade of red with a darker line between, exhibited in the two dolls at
left, are features of the Alt, Beck & Gottschalck porcelain factory.[6]

Fig. 153
Girl
Nauendorf, Thuringia, Germany
Attributed to Alt, Beck & Gottschalck
About 1860-70
Incised in shoulder plate: A10
Decorated parian-type shoulder head with
pierced ears and crystal bead earrings, molded painted blonde hair with braids on sides,
tall curls at top of head, sausage curls and
braid in back woven through molded black
ribbon, painted blue eyes with clear highlights, shoulder plate with molded gold pendant on black band and white ruffle down
both sides of neck and blue bow at V of
bodice, old cloth body with new kid arms,
cotton chemise, slip, and lace-trimmed
ankle-length pantalets, organdy petticoat
h 22 ¹/₂"
20-06-45
Chandler Collection, 1962-262.114

Lady
Nauendorf, Thuringia, Germany (head)
Attributed to Alt, Beck & Gottschalck
About 1875
Philadelphia, Pennsylvania, United States
(body)
Jacob Lacmann
Stamped on back of each leg: J
Lacmann's/Patent/March 24th, 1874
1874-83
Decorated parian-type shoulder head with
ears pierced into head and coral drop earrings, molded painted blonde hair with curls
on top framing crown with molded gold
beads in front, pink flowers or proper right
ear and large waves and sausage curls in
back, painted blue eyes, coral pendant, manufactured cloth swing-jointed body with stiff
mitten hands and delineated fingers, crepe,
organdy, and lace dress, leather boots
h 19 ³/₄"
20-06-24
Chandler Collection, 1962-262.84

Lady
Nauendorf, Thuringia, Germany
Attributed to Alt, Beck & Gottschalck
About 1880
Decorated parian-type shoulder head with
pierced ears and gold dangle earrings, molded painted blonde hair with bangs swept up
into high pompadour and molded black
beads across center, cascading into loose
curls at rear, molded yoke with burgundy-
edged smocking and iron cross suspended
from black "velvet" necklace ("Kaiserin
Augusta" style), painted blue eyes with white
highlights, new cloth swing-jointed body
with leather arms, redressed in embroidered
silk dress by Mrs. George Chandler
h 22"
20-06-46
Chandler Collection, 1962-262.84

These three elegant ladies all have elaborate coiffures with molded decoration as well as
pierced ears and earrings. The dolls on either end are further embellished with modeled
shoulder plates simulating jewelry as well as a ruffled bodice and collar. The body of the doll
in the middle was patented by Joseph Lacmann in 1874. His invention consisted of gluing a
molded papier-mâché hand or foot within the cloth covering for the appropriate limb. In this
case, her mitten-shaped hands are stiff and immoveable.

Fig. 154
Lady
Ohrdruf, Thuringia, Germany
Attributed to Kestner & Co.
About 1860
Parian-type shoulder head with pierced ears
and simulated gold and turquoise drop ear-
ings, molded painted blonde hair swept
away from face with large braid around head
and molded bow in back over cascade of
sausage curls, applied lace hair band cut
from same fabric as dress, painted blue eyes
with highlights, new cloth swing-jointed
body with leather arms, redressed by Mrs. F.
C. Jeffries in old silk dress, cotton pantalets,
silk petticoat, damask shoes
h 22"
20-06-42
Chandler Collection, 1962-262.111

Lady
Gräfenroda, Thuringia, Germany
Attributed to Dornheim, Koch & Fischer
About 1880-90
Parian-type shoulder head, molded painted
café-au-lait hair in curly flat-top style with
applied pink roses and green leaves in center and on both sides, painted blue eyes
with highlights, cloth swing-jointed body
with leather lower arms, pink silk dress, cotton undergarments
h 19 1/2"
20-06-06
Webb Collection, 1952-60

Lady
Gräfenroda, Thuringia, Germany
Dornheim, Koch & Fischer
About 1880-90
Decorated parian-type shoulder head, molded painted blonde hair swept away from face
and tied into rolled bun in back with molded
blue luster scarf topped with gold and pink
flowers over head and leaves falling to her
left, painted blue glazed eyes with white
highlights, painted mouth, new cloth swing-
jointed body with leather arms, redressed by
Mrs. George Chandler in pink silk dress
h 21"
20-06-41
Chandler Collection, 1962-262.110

Due to her undecorated coiffure, the doll on the left may represent an earlier parian-type.
The distinctive unpainted space between her small, pursed mouth and slightly smiling lips
suggests she is a very rare surviving example from Kestner & Co., a factory known primarily
for its china dolls.[7] In contrast, the two ladies attributed to the factory of Dornheim, Koch &
Fischer exhibit extraordinarily fine workmanship in the Meissen genre with exquisitely detailed
hair ornaments consisting of molded roses, harebells, and leaves clustered around the
head.[8]

Fig. 155
Lady
Gräfenroda, Thuringia, Germany
Attributed to Dornheim, Koch &
Fischer
About 1860-70
Decorated parian-type shoulder
head, molded painted cafe-au-lait
hair parted in front and pulled
into molded blue scarf trimmed
in gold stars and blue dots,
molded shoulder yoke with open-
molded collar blouse trimmed
with glazed pink lapels, blue
painted eyes with white highlights, old cloth swing-jointed
body with china lower arms, silk
dress, oilcloth boots
h 16 3/4"
20-06-36
Chandler Collection, 1961-
262.105

Lady
Pössneck, Thuringia, Germany
Attributed to Conta & Böhme
About 1860-70
Incised on outside of back shoulder plate: 24
Decorated parian-type shoulder
head with pierced ears and
turquoise and pearl drop earrings, molded painted black hair
with center part and wave over
forehead with brush marks on
sides and swept up into molded
blue band with side sausage
curls going down back of head,
painted blue eyes with white
highlights, homemade cloth
swing-jointed body with white
unglazed arms, silk twill dress by
Mrs. George Chandler copied
from one worn by Empress
Charlotte of Mexico
h 25 1/2"
20-06-43
Chandler Collection, 1961-262.112

The lady at left has an unusual hair decoration consisting of a blue
scarf trimmed in gold stars—a gilding process that requires additional
firing—combined with the pink collar detail, a feature Mary Krombholz
has associated with the products of Dornheim, Koch & Fischer. The
doll at right exhibits the rarer black, rather than blonde, hair.

Fig. 156
Boy
Gräfenroda, Thuringia, Germany
Attributed to Dornheim, Koch & Fischer
About 1860-70
Decorated parian-type shoulder head, molded painted blonde hair with side part
and brush marks sweeping up off forehead in swirl ending in three curls and pouf
on either side terminating in three horizontal rolls, painted blue eyes with white
highlights, painted mouth with darker line separating lips, molded white yoke with
collar and blue- and-gold tie at neck tucking down front of shirt, old cloth swing-
jointed body with replaced kid arms, wool pants, velvet jacket, flowered velvet
waistcoat, flannel trousers, cotton striped stockings, stitched fabric shoes
h 20 1/2"
20-06-02
Webb Collection, 1952-60

This dashing cavalier with curled upswept hairdo is known as the "Dresden
Gentleman" in America. His distinctive modeled and painted dress shirt with its
collar and tie has been associated with shoulder heads produced at the Dornheim,
Koch & Fischer porcelain factory. Furthermore, Mary Krombholz has identified the
same doll with a similar body stamped on the chest "Leipold"—the name of the
New York toy shop from which the doll originally came and where his cloth body
was probably made.[9] This example shows some discoloration on the chest that
may be the location of the now-missing "Leipold" stamp.

Fig. 157
Lady
Nauendorf, Thuringia, Germany
Alt, Beck & Gottschalck[10]
About 1880
Incised inside shoulder plate: 12 (or 72)
Painted in red inside shoulder plate: 2
Printed in black at top back of cloth
body: 7
Lightly tinted unglazed shoulder head
with pierced ears and coral flower earrings, café-au-lait hair swept up from
face, brass tiara with metal beads
across front, large waves of hair across
top and on back of head, blue glass
eyes with painted upper and lower lashes, painted feathered eyebrows, peach
mouth with darker line through center,
old cloth swing-jointed body with
leather arms slip-covered in cloth and
china hands, striped cotton stockings,
cotton and lace-trimmed chemise, petticoat, and pantalets, leather boots with
scalloped stitching on side
26 1/2"
20-06-51
Chandler Collection, 1962-262.120

In addition to her striking blue glass
eyes and richly coiffed café-au-lait hair,
extraordinary and rare is the ornamental brass tiara with metal beads
attached with wires through holes in
the head. The doll's headdress can be
removed to allow the use of changeable
hair ornaments—an innovative idea
that surprisingly was not employed
more often. This decorated shoulder
head is attached to an unusual cloth
body with sewn-on striped stockings
and red leather boots. Her unusual
large and well-molded china hands with
traces of red around each nail are identical to the china bride (fig. 109). They
are attached to leather arms probably
using the method patented in 1860 by
Martin Kintzback of Philadelphia, which
uses cork to conceal the rough edges of
the joint.

Fig. 158
Lady
Ohrdruf, Thuringia, Germany
Attributed to C.F. Kling & Co.
About 1860-70
Parian-type head with swivel neck
on unglazed porcelain breast
plate, pierced ears with crystal
pear-shaped earrings, molded
painted blonde hair with center
part and swept up on both sides
into applied cascade of curls,
dark blue glass eyes with painted
upper and lower lashes, brows
with fine lines inside larger line,
old cloth swing-jointed body with
leather hands, redressed by Mrs.
F. C. Jeffries in green silk walking
suit with lace at sleeves
h 17"
20-06-48
Chandler Collection, 1962-262.117

Lady
Ohrdruf, Thuringia, Germany
Attributed to C.F. Kling & Co.
About 1860-70
Decorated parian-type shoulder
head with pierced ears and pearl
earrings, molded painted ash
blonde hair pulled away from
face and braided into molded
cranberry and gold ribbon running from front to back, blue
glass eyes with painted upper
and lower lashes, high coloring
on cheeks, manufactured cloth
swing-jointed body with leather
arms, redressed by Marta
Mengis in 1963 from old silk and
velvet fabric
h 15 1/2"
20-06-31
Chandler Collection, 1962-
262.100

The regal doll on the left has an extraordinary number of rare features, including glass inset eyes, a coiffure with separately modeled
and applied curls, and a neck that swivels. A metal threaded armature
secures the head to the shoulder plate below, and the applied curls at
the rear conceal the hole through which the neck joint is inserted. A
pivoting head is a feature usually reserved for bisque dolls.[11] The
shape of the earlobes, which flare out and curl up slightly, is a characteristic of Kling models.

Fig. 159
Lady
Nauendorf, Thuringia, Germany
Attributed to Alt, Beck & Gottschalck
About 1880
Parian-type shoulder head, human hair wig,
painted blue eyes, painted mouth with line
through center, cloth swing-jointed body
with wood lower limbs and flat feet with
black painted shoes, cotton dress
h 10 3/4"
20-01-50
Gift of Mr. and Mrs. Donald Cram, 1955-611.1

Lady
Pössneck, Thuringia, Germany
Attributed to Conta & Böhme
About 1860
Painted in red on inside left side of shoulder
plate: VI
Decorated parian-type shoulder head, molded painted black hair with two molded red
bows and comb with traces of red paint, old
cloth swing-jointed body with lower china
limbs and black flat slipper feet, silk taffeta
dress
h 8 1/2"
20-06-38
Chandler Collection, 1962-262.107

Both of these very small parian-type dolls
are distinguished by their hair treatment.
The coiffure on the porcelain shoulder head
has a widow's peak and hairline brush
marks in front and a protruding bow in the
rear; it has been painted black and then
glazed to a lustrous sheen. In contrast, the
lady on the left was fitted with a rare human
hair wig.

Fig. 160
Lady
Gräfenroda, Thuringia, Germany
Stamped on chest fabric: no 6
Dornheim, Koch & Fischer
About 1860-70
Decorated parian-type shoulder
head, molded painted brown hair
parted in front and swept away
from face in bouffant style, decorated with applied brown luster
ruching of ribbon all around back
of head securing snood and leaving fall of hair down on neck,
molded and decorated white
blouse with pink bow and some
gold trim, painted blue eyes,
closed mouth, cloth swing-jointed body with leather arms, lace-
trimmed petticoat and chemise,
leather shoes
h 20 1/2"
20-06-49
Chandler Collection, 1962-262.118

Girl
Nauendorf, Thuringia, Germany
Alt, Beck & Gottschalck
About 1860-70
Decorated parian-type shoulder
head, molded painted light
brown hair pulled away from face
and encased in molded beaded
snood with two blue ribbons at
side, painted blue eyes with highlights, closed mouth with deep
dimples on each side of chin,
new cloth swing-jointed body
with leather arms, redressed by
Mrs. George Chandler in dotted-
swiss dress
h 19 1/4"
20-06-33
Chandler Collection, 1962-
262.102

Both of these dolls illustrate the popularity of hairnets, or snoods,
during the 1860s and 1870s. In addition, the doll at left has the more
unusual brown hair and an applied, glazed ceramic ruching around
her head.

Fig. 161
Lady
Ohrdruf, Thuringia, Germany
C.F. Kling & Co.
About 1860-70
Decorated tinted unglazed porcelain shoulder head turned to side with pierced ears, turquoise drop earrings and matching necklace, molded painted blonde hair with tight ringlets all around face pulled back into cascade of curls held by molded black bow, painted blue eyes with white highlights, closed mouth with darker line between lips, French kid body with gusseted knees and elbows, redressed in silk gown
h 20 1/4"
20-06-05
Webb Collection, 1952-60

Lady
Ohrdruf, Thuringia, Germany
Attributed to C.F. Kling & Co.
About 1860-70
Incised on back of shoulder plate: 144-8
Decorated tinted unglazed porcelain shoulder head with pierced ears and brown luster drop earrings, molded painted hair with curls on forehead pulled back to form sausage curls in back, molded black comb and blue ostrich plumes, molded white neck ruffle decorated with molded yellow rose in neckline, brown glass eyes with painted upper and lower lashes, painted feathered eyebrows, new cloth body with old curved unglazed porcelain arms, old unglazed porcelain legs and purple boots with a wash of gold luster, purple line-decorated stockings, redressed by Mrs. George Chandler in old pearl-decorated fabric based on pattern created in Paris for Mrs. Tom Thumb for reception in honor of P. T. Barnum's famous midgets
h 21 1/2"
20-06-39
Chandler Collection, 1962-262.108

Each of these blonde decorated ladies exhibits unusual modeling techniques. The doll on the left has a stationary turned head. Her companion on the right with stunning glass eyes, a molded hair comb with an ostrich feather, and a distinctive stand-up collar has been attributed to the C.F. Kling porcelain factory based on an almost identical marked example.[12]

Fig. 162
Lady
Gräfenroda, Thuringia, Germany
Attributed to Dornheim, Koch &
Fischer
About 1870
Tinted unglazed porcelain shoulder head with pierced ears and turquoise and purple luster drop earrings, café-au-lait hair with center part and two loops at forehead winged on sides and roped in back in two sections, painted blue eyes with highlights, painted mouth with darker line between lips, rounded double ruff of lace molded around neck and at top of guimpe, new cloth body swing-jointed at shoulders, hips, and knees, old kid arms, redressed by Mrs. George Chandler in silk walking dress trimmed in lace, cotton pantalets and slip trimmed in lace and blue ribbon
h 22"
20-06-44
Chandler Collection, 1962-262.113

Lady
Gräfenroda, Thuringia, Germany
Attributed to Dornheim, Koch &
Fischer
About 1870
Decorated parian-type porcelain shoulder head with pierced ears and earrings, molded painted blonde hair with center part and molded pink bow and real brown feather, two puffs of short curls at top pulled to back above ears into rolls and curls, painted blue eyes with highlights, painted mouth with darker line between lips, square ruff of lace molded around neck with gold beads, cloth swing-jointed body and lower leather arms, redressed by Mrs. George Chandler in silk walking dress decorated with coral beads made from antique fabric and brass chain link pocket (purse) attached to jacket
h 17 1/4"
20-06-53
Chandler Collection, 1962-262.122

These elegant ladies illustrate 1870s hairstyles, which featured loops or puffs at the forehead pulled up at the sides with either rolls or braided ropes in back. The coiffure of each is complimented by ornate molded and painted three-dimensional ruffs at the neck and elaborate silk costumes below. Dornheim Koch & Fischer clearly studied the fashion plates of the time and modeled their lady dolls after these printed sources. The share the same long oval face and darker line between the lips characteristic of dolls molded and painted at this factory.[13]

Fig. 163
Lady
Nauendorf, Thuringia, Germany
Attributed to Alt, Beck & Gottschalck
About 1880
Queen Louise (blue scarf) parian-type shoulder head, molded painted blonde hair, molded blue scarf draped around head, blue glass eyes, painted feathered eyebrows, painted upper and lower lashes, new cotton swing-jointed body with leather arms, redressed by Mrs. F. C. Jeffries in silk and lace gown with velvet bows, cotton slip, leather shoes
h 19 1/2"
20-06-54
Chandler Collection, 1962-262.123

This portrait doll is said to suggest Queen Louise of Prussia (1776-1810) as the German artist Gustav Richter (1823-84) depicted her descending the stairs at Schönbrunn Palace in Vienna, Austria, on her way to Napoleon to plead for her people. Queen Louise took the initiative to contact the czar of Russia and king of Austria, both of whom, along with her husband, King Frederick William III of Prussia, signed the Potsdam Treaty in 1805. The treaty resulted in an alliance among these three nations against Napoleon, who later termed Louise "my beautiful enemy" for her role in forming this pact.[14] This doll is most distinctive for the modeled blue scarf that wraps around her head as well as for her striking blue glass eyes.

Fig. 164

Lady
Pössneck, Thuringia, Germany
Attributed to Conta & Böhme
About 1870
Decorated parian-type shoulder head, molded painted blonde hair with molded blue snood with pink tassel and molded blue-and-white feather ("Empress Eugénie" style), painted blue eyes, painted mouth, cloth swing-jointed body at shoulders, hips, and knees, bisque lower arms and legs with bulbous calves and molded pink boots with heels, silk and cotton petticoats, new cotton chemise based on old pattern
19"
20-06-55
Chandler Collection, 1962-262.124

Lady
Nauendorf, Thuringia, Germany
Attributed to Alt, Beck & Gottschalck
United States (clockwork mechanism patented by Enoch Rice Morrison July 15, 1862)
1862
Stenciled in black ink on bottom of base: Atopiticaon/Patented July, 15, 1862, also in Europe, 20 DEC, 1862
Decorated parian-type shoulder head, molded painted hair with molded white-and-purple luster scarf with gold trim and blue snood ("Empress Eugénie" style), painted blue eyes with highlights and lashes, closed mouth, wire, carton, and wood body with leather arms, cotton dress, metal boots
10"
20-06-13
Webb Collection, 1952-60

Lady
Nauendorf, Thuringia, Germany
Attributed to Alt, Beck & Gottschalck
About 1860
Decorated parian-type shoulder head, molded painted blonde hair with molded purple- and-white luster scarf with gold trim and blue snood ("Empress Eugénie" style), painted blue eyes with white highlights and lashes, closed mouth, cloth swing-jointed body with lower unglazed porcelain limbs and black flat slippers, costume made from wide ribbons
13"
20-06-11
Webb Collection, 1952-60

Although they were not portrait dolls, the faces and coiffures of such models as these—with their feathers, snoods and scarves—suggested the beautiful and elegant Spanish-born Empress Eugénie, wife of

French Emperor Napoleon III (ruled 1852-1870), to later collectors. According to Queen Victoria's journal, Eugénie was gentle, pleasing, charming, lively, and vivacious.[15] These dolls' heads show several variations of the Eugénie hairstyle and face, and while the dolls seem very similar they do differ greatly in modeling, coloration, and glazing. A version (20-06-13) has even been attached to a rare mechanical toy called an autoperipatetikos (from the Greek word meaning "walking about by itself"). It consisted of a doll head mounted on a body with an ample, crinoline-shaped base that concealed a strong, key-wound clockwork mechanism. This device operated little metal feet in a steady step-by-step walk.

Fig. 165
Lady
Ohrdruf, Thuringia, Germany (head)
Attributed to C.F. Kling & Co.
Covington, Kentucky (body)
Philip Goldsmith
1885
Incised on back of shoulder plate: 128-11
Stamped in purple old English lettering on front of body: My Dolly
Stamped in black in old English lettering on back of body: 8
Decorated parian-type shoulder head, pierced ears with pearl and gold glass-bead earrings, molded painted blonde hair with curly bangs swept up into molded black side comb at top and sides and mass of curls on back of head, blue threaded-glass eyes, painted feathered brows, painted upper and lower lashes, cloth body, stamped-on blue and black color in shape of corset (in front only) with three black striped lines in front and one line with buttons in front center trimmed on edges with white-and-red baby rickrack, swing-jointed at hips and knees, blue-striped lower legs with attached lavender bands at top, pink leather boots laced with string tassels, lower white kid arms, redressed by Mrs. George Chandler in silk brocade and lace wedding dress, cotton chemise, pantalets, petticoat with train and quilted bustle, including nosegay and bustle, kid shoes
h 26"
20-06-58
Chandler Collection, 1962-262.135

Philip Goldsmith—an Austrian immigrant to Covington, Kentucky—patented (#332,248) his unique cloth doll bodies with realistic printed stockings, leather boots with laces and double tassels, and an integral corset with stamped lacings edged with applied rickrack braid. They were sold either separately through the Montgomery Ward catalogs or with imported porcelain (such as here) or, later, composition heads. According to an article published in *Playthings* Magazine in December 1908, "The finger stitching was guided by small sticks about the size of match sticks which were inserted in the leather." As she stated in her autobiography, written between 1904 and 1918, Goldsmith's wife, who had been a dressmaker at one time, made the patterns and assisted in dressing the dolls by 1879. However, the Shelburne Museum's "my dolly" was costumed by Mrs. George Chandler in an elaborate silk brocade and lace wedding dress and cotton underwear complete with a quilted bustle.

Fig. 166
Girl
Katzhütte, Thuringia, Germany
Attributed to Hertwig & Co.
About 1900
Incised on back of shoulder plate: 3 C
Decorated-bonnet parian-type shoulder
head, molded painted light blonde bangs
with molded bonnet, white ruching, and
blue bows, painted blue eyes, closed mouth
with space between, old cloth swing-jointed
body with lower unglazed porcelain arms,
redressed in wool dress by Mrs. George
Chandler
h 20 1/2"
20-06-26
Chandler Collection, 1962-262.91

Girl
Katzhütte, Thuringia, Germany
Attributed to Hertwig & Co.
About 1900
Decorated-bonnet stone-bisque shoulder
head, molded painted blonde hair with
molded tam-o'-shanter-type hat, square
molded yoke with molded gold-painted
necklace, painted blue eyes, new cloth
swing-jointed body with leather arms,
redressed in silk dress by Mrs. F. C. Jeffries
h 17"
20-06-30
Chandler Collection, 1962-262.95

Girl
Katzhütte, Thuringia, Germany
Attributed to Hertwig & Co.
About 1900
Decorated-bonnet parian-type shoulder
head, molded painted blonde hair with
molded winter tam-type hat with molded fur
band, shoulder plate with molded fur and
gold trim, painted blue eyes, new cloth
swing-jointed body with leather arms,
redressed by Mrs. George Chandler in wool
coat and leather roller skates, first advertised in *Playthings* in 1905
h 18"
20-06-27
Chandler Collection, 1962-262.92

Girl
Katzhütte, Thuringia, Germany
Attributed to Hertwig & Co
About 1900
Decorated-bonnet stone-bisque shoulder
head, molded painted light blonde hair
under molded shell-type blue bonnet, molded blouse trimmed in gold, painted blue
eyes, new cloth swing-jointed body with
leather arms and boots, redressed in old
lace dress by Mrs. F. C. Jeffries
h 16 3/4"
20-06-25
Chandler Collection, 1962-262.90

Fig. 167
Girl
Katzhütte, Thuringia, Germany
Attributed to Hertwig & Co.
About 1900
Decorated-bonnet stone-bisque shoulder
head, molded painted pale blonde hair with
molded, glazed, and gold-trimmed clovers
on head and breast plate, blue painted eyes,
original twill swing-jointed body with red
stripe down center, china lower limbs
h 13"
20-06-60
Webb Collection, 1952-60

These unmarked bonnet-headed dolls are
often composed of stone bisque—a material
that is coarser and grainier in texture than
parian ware. The Hertwig & Co. porcelain
factory made a large number of figurines
with fanciful hats and used some of these
same molds for bonnet-headed dolls starting in 1865. This grouping illustrates the
variety of whimsical headgear imitating
straw and fur as well as scallop shells and
even four-leaf clovers, which Hertwig & Co.
made only for the New York importer Butler
Brothers.[7]

Dolls of Cloth
and Other Materials

Cloth dolls are those with heads and bodies made completely of fabric. They generally are soft, lightweight, unbreakable, and often washable, as well as eminently huggable. Historically, they were often a child's first homemade toy and were on the whole less sophisticated than dolls produced from other materials. They were popular playthings but, unfortunately, they were not very sturdy. As a result, fewer survive than any other type of doll.

The Shelburne Museum collection includes two basic categories—homemade and manufactured cloth dolls originating in Europe and America. For the first time, enterprising women including Izannah Walker (active 1855-about 1886) and Martha Jenks Chase (active 1880s-1925) in the United States and Käthe Kruse (active 1904-1930) in Germany provided a viable alternative to consumers. American makers successfully identified materials such as stockinet fabric, stuffed with cotton batting, and waterproof zinc-based paint, among other things, to create soft, washable, and durable dolls. The development of inexpensive chromolithography techniques enabled commercial manufacturers to print dolls with facial features on cloth that homemakers could cut out, stuff, and sew together. Enterprising doll makers also patented unusual materials such as hard rubber as well as metal for dolls' heads, which enjoyed a brief period of popularity but in the long run could not compete with the more traditional ceramic alternatives.

Fig. 168
Child
Central Falls, Rhode Island, United States
Izannah Walker
about 1870
Cloth stationary head, oil-painted brown hair, brown painted eyes with white highlights, black upper and lower eyeliner and line at crease, painted feathered brows, light red dots in corners and in nostrils, applied ears, cloth swing-jointed body with painted lower limbs, hand with four delineated fingers together and separate thumb, oil-painted black boots with laces, cotton and lace-trimmed dress
19"
10-03-193
Webb Collection, 1952-60

The first recorded American woman doll manufacturer is Izannah Walker of Rhode Island whose goal, according to her patent specifications, was to produce playable dolls that were "easily kept clean and not apt to injure a young child which may fall on it. It will preserve its appearance for a long time as the soft secondary stuffing under the stockinet or external webbing enables it to give under pressure so that the oil paint will not scale off. At the same time the inner and more compact stuffing prevents ordinary pressure from forcing the surface in to such an extent as to crack the paint."[1] One of the most distinctive features of the Izannah Walker dolls is the manner in which their hair is painted. This girl's ringlet curls hanging in front of the ear recreate those depicted in nineteenth-century folk art portraits of American children.

Fig. 169
Three Ladies
Possibly United States
About 1768-80
Rolled-cloth heads and bodies of old homespun fabric, traces of human-hair wigs, stitched thread features, rolled-cloth arms over wire, no legs, original cotton and silk gowns, net and ribbon hats
h 7-8"
20-3-222-224
Estate of Helen Smith Spalding Best, 1994-40.2-.4

Lady
United States
About 1900
Polished cotton stationary head, glued-on cotton wool hair, silk embroidered blue eyes, eyebrows, eyelid, and mouth, one-piece unjointed cloth body with cloth limbs, gauze dress with large picture hat
h 12"
20-03-141
Webb Collection, 1952-60

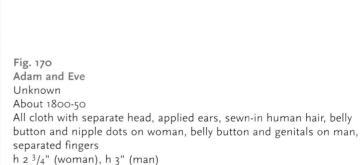

According to a handwritten note accompanying these dolls, the three small girls were made for a relative of Fanny Manning Swallow in 1768. The doll with the empire-style dress (second from right), with its high waist, long sleeves puffed at the cap, and black apron, was redressed for Swallow in 1805. Constructed of rolled cloth—a material used for dolls in the eighteenth century[2]—their stitched thread facial features were covered in a sheer fabric and secured at the neck with a ribbon.

The lithe, graceful lady (20-03-141) is attired in the stylish dress and enormous hat associated with Gibson Girls, created by American illustrator Charles Gibson for *Life Magazine* about 1890 (see fig. 134).

Fig. 170
Adam and Eve
Unknown
About 1800-50
All cloth with separate head, applied ears, sewn-in human hair, belly button and nipple dots on woman, belly button and genitals on man, separated fingers
h 2 3/4" (woman), h 3" (man)
20-03-79
Chandler Collection, 1962-262.154a and b

This remarkable pair of Adam and Eve-type dolls is one of a handful known to exist in public collections such as the Strong Museum in Rochester, New York, and the Historical Society of Carroll County in Westminster, Maryland. These commercially made figures[3] probably once had clothes, now unfortunately lost. Measuring only three inches high and assembled in seven unjointed sections stitched together, the facial features and anatomically correct components are executed in soft sculpture using silk thread.

Fig. 171
Child
Central Falls, Rhode Island, United States
Izannah Walker
About 1870
Cloth stationary head, oil-painted brown
hair, applied ears, oil-painted brown eyes,
closed mouth, cloth swing-jointed cloth
body with painting to lower arms and mid-
legs, sewn-on stockings, old cotton dress,
and possibly original cotton underclothes
h 19 3/4"
20-03-192
Webb Collection, 1952-60

Child
Central Falls, Rhode Island, United States
Izannah Walker
About 1870
Cloth stationary head, oil-painted brown
hair, brown painted eyes with white highlights, painted feathered brows, painted
black upper and lower eyeliner and line at
crease, slight red dots in corners and in nostrils, applied ears, swing-jointed cloth body
with painted lower limbs, four delineated fingers and separate thumb, oil-painted black
boots with laces, cotton and lace-trimmed
dress
h 19"
20-03-193
Webb Collection, 1952-60

Child
Central Falls, Rhode Island, United States
Izannah Walker
About 1870
Cloth stationary head, oil-painted brown
hair, applied ears, cloth swing-jointed body
with painted lower limbs, oil-painted black
boots with laces, cotton chemise
h 19"
20-03-194
Webb Collection, 1952-60

Although she was crafting her dolls as a home industry as early as the 1850s, in 1873
Izannah Walker obtained a patent for her complicated process, which involved coating cloth
with paste and pressing it in a die. The molded head then had a layer of cotton batting and a
layer of stockinet applied to the outside after which it was re-pressed in the mold. The inside
of the head was then stuffed quite firmly and reinforced with a central piece of wood. This
technique gave the doll's head the ability to give slightly under pressure, which helped prevent the finished coating of oil paint from pealing or chipping. The ears were not molded as
part of the head but applied separately. Walker sewed the hands and feet by hand and then
painted the completed doll in oil colors. The Walker-style low boot with laces is distinctive,
although some dolls were barefoot with stitched toes.

Fig. 172
African American Lady
Pawtucket, Rhode Island, United
States
Martha Jenks Chase
About 1890
Printed cardboard label sewn on
back: The Chase Stockinet
Doll/Made of Stockinet and
Cloth./Stuffed with
Cotton./Made by Hand./Made
by Especially Trained Workers
Cloth stationary head, black
mohair wig, painted features,
applied ears, cloth swing-jointed
body with painted lower limbs,
cotton dress with apron
h 26"
20-03-30
Webb Collection, 1952-60

Child
Pawtucket, Rhode Island, United
States
Martha Jenks Chase
About 1900
Printed paper label on back: The
Chase Stockinet Doll/Made of
Stockinet and Cloth./Stuffed
with Cotton./Made by
Hand./Made by Especially
Trained Workers.
Stamped on proper left top leg:
Chase Trademark/Made in
U.S.A.
Cloth stationary head, oil-paint-
ed blonde hair, oil-painted
brown eyes with painted upper
lashes, closed mouth, sateen
swing-jointed body with lower
oil-painted limbs
h 16 1/2"
20-03-63
Chandler Collection, 1962-
262.20

Child
Pawtucket, Rhode Island, United
States
Martha Jenks Chase
1890
Stamped on proper left leg:
Chase Trademark/Made in
U.S.A.
Stamped on proper left leg:
Chase Trademark/Made in
U.S.A.
Cloth stationary head, oil-paint-
ed blonde hair, oil-painted
brown eyes with painted upper
lashes, sateen swing-jointed
body with lower oil-painted limb
h 23 3/4"
20-03-31
Webb Collection, 1952-60

Baby
Bad Kösen, Germany
Käthe Kruse
About 1925
Stamped on proper left foot:
control numbers [illegible]
Cloth stationary head, hand-
painted brown hair with brush
strokes around face, hand -
painted features, stockinet body
swing-jointed at shoulder and
legs
h 16 3/4"
20-03-26
Webb Collection, 1952-60

Martha Chase dolls were available in adult, children, baby, as well as ethnic models of all sizes to instruct mothers and young girls how to feed, bathe, and dress their offspring. In 1913 Chase even produced life-size models designed as a teaching aid with which nurses and other hospital personnel could practice routine treatment procedures involving all body irrigations, eliminations, and the administration of syringe needles. The "Chase Hospital Mannequin" was equipped with special features including a rubberized interior, immersible body, and holes in the nostrils and ears. Chase dolls made during the firm's early years have sateen torsos, such as the ones shown here, while later versions dating from the 1920s have stockinet bodies with a waterproof finish.

German doll maker Käthe Kruse spent years developing a soft and lifelike cloth doll with a realistic face and proportionate, moveable, and firmly stuffed bodies. Kruse described the doll as "indestructible" and as "an education toward motherliness" when it was first marketed in 1912. Starting at home with five women to help her with the sewing, stuffing, and painting, by 1939 she had turned an old school into a fac-tory and employed one hundred twenty people who produced approximately twelve thousand dolls each year.[4] Many Kruse dolls have indi-vidualistic, poignant expressions based on the faces of her own seven children or those of the cherubs in Renaissance paintings.[5] They were always considered prestigious toys appreciated for the quality of their construction as well as for their aesthetic beauty.

Fig. 173
Child
Pawtucket, Rhode Island, United States
Martha Jenks Chase
About 1895
Cloth stationary head, painted blonde hair, painted blue eyes, painted upper lashes, applied ears, closed mouth, sateen body with square neckline and swing-jointed at shoulders, elbows, hips, and knees, bare feet with stitched toes, applied thumbs, cotton two-piece dress
h 16"
20-05-127
Estate of Constance Ayer, 1982-25.7

Possession of a cloth child made by Izannah Walker of Central Falls, Rhode Island, inspired Martha Jenks Chase to design her own dolls. As the daughter and wife of a physician and raised by a socially concerned mother, Chase was a staunch supporter of the Progressive movement of the time. For her seven children she accordingly created durable and lovable playthings that had practical as well as artistic appeal. Cleanliness and hygiene were important considerations in her designs, and her advertising stressed that the dolls "could be washed with warm water keeping infecting germs from our babies."[6]

From 1889 through the 1930s Chase produced her sturdy dolls in a small workshop behind her house with a small group of female employees and sold her products to such department stores as Gimbels and Macy's. The faces were made by pressing wet stockinet, glue, and plaster between a two-part indented metal and raised plaster mold. After the mask dried, it was stitched to a second piece of fabric and then stuffed with balls of cotton to form the head. The face, arms, and legs were painted with waterproof oils to make them completely impermeable and washable. Such characteristics were important in teaching young girls good hygienic habits, which it was presumed they would practice when they became older.

Fig. 174
King George VI and Queen Elizabeth
London, England
Liberty & Co.
1939
Printed tag on clothing: Liberty/made in London
Paper with them reads: King George VI Coronation
May 12, 1937, International Doll House, Krug Chinese
Imports, 2227 St. Paul St., Baltimore MD.
Cloth stationary heads with seam down center of face,
fiber wigs, needle-sculpted and painted features,
unjointed linen bodies, original dressed in Liberty of
London fabrics, of old silk and velvet
h 10"
0-03-74 ab
Chandler Collection, 1962-262.129, 130

Liberty of London was established in 1873 as a fabric shop and trademarked a line of "Art Dolls" in 1920 made from their textile remnants. In this cottage industry, artisans were not allowed to sign or take individual credit for the products. The most famous of these were the set of figures produced in 1939 for the coronation of King George VI which included dolls representing members of the wedding party. Their features are needle-sculpted and hand-painted with a center seam in their faces and wire armatures in their linen bodies. The king wears a crown of red velvet with a wire crescent covered with gold foil and enhanced by multi-

colored glass and rhinestones. His matching robe is bordered in white felt embroidered with black lines to represent the ermine tails used in the attire of royalty. Underneath a red tunic with gold braiding, white satin knee-length trousers with knit stockings and black leather shoes complete the costume. His queen wears a white satin gown embroidered in gold with lace sleeves, a matching red robe trimmed in "ermine," and a crown with crystal rhinestones and a faux sapphire.

Fig. 175
Boy
European
About 1930
Felt swivel head, blonde mohair wig sewn in swirls, painted brown eyes with white highlights and black line around white portion, painted brows and upper lashes, red dots in nostrils, two-toned red painted mouth, all-felt body with disk-jointed arms, stitched fingers with separate thumb, legs wire-and-button-jointed with patch covering button, original knit sweater and wool cap
h 13"
20-03-152
Museum Collection, 2004-5

Girl
Spain
Arte Tomalidad Ingenio
About 1930
Pressed board tag on back of dress: Madrid N. A. T. I
Paper tag on back of dress: Made in Spain/Novedad
Felt swivel head, mohair wig on cheesecloth cap, painted gray eyes with two highlights, painted brows and brown upper lashes, red dots in nostrils, two-toned red painted lips, all-felt body with disk-jointed arms and stitching at top, two middle fingers stitched together, legs joined by button-and-wire swivel with a patch over button, two-piece legs with side darts, original felt clothing
h 14"
20-03-153
Museum Collection, 20-04-6

Girl
Turin, Italy
Enrico and Elena Scavini (Lenci)
About 1930
Printed cloth tag sewn on outside of dress: Lenci made in Italy
Cardboard tag under slip: "Bamboli a Italia/Lenci/Torino/made in Italy
Felt swivel head, black mohair wig, painted side-glancing brown eyes with highlights, painted brows and upper lashes, two-toned red painted lips, applied ears, dimple in chin, felt body with swivel disk-joints at shoulders and hips, original felt and organdy clothing
h 16 1/4"
20-03-90
Webb Collection, 1952-60

Girl
Turin, Italy
Enrico and Elena Scavini (Lenci)
About 1930
Felt swivel head, light brown mohair wig, painted eyes with white highlights, painted brows and upper lashes, two-toned red painted lips, applied ears, felt body with swivel disk-joints at arms and legs, bent arms, original felt dress and straw broom
h 9 1/2"
20-03-91
Webb Collection, 1952-60

Felt dolls were made in various parts of Europe and imaginatively costumed to represent a variety of personalities. However, the Lenci dolls were completely original, as was their construction. Their invention was the use of a two-part die that made it possible to mold the entire head in one piece without a center seam. The facial features were painted and included the use of white highlights on the iris of the typical side-glancing eyes, which gives Lenci dolls a surprised look. The startled expressions were perhaps meant to represent eager and inquisitive youngsters, the sort parents of the time might wish to cultivate. Their distinctive pursed mouths are heart shaped with a lighter pink tone for the bottom lip and a redder tint for the top.

Fig. 176
Girl
Turin, Italy
Enrico and Elena Scavini (Lenci)
About 1940-50
Silver round tag with blue writing on back of
neck: Lenci/Torino/made in Italy
Felt swivel head, cap wig of stitched felt
curls, blue oval patch-felt eyes, applied ears,
felt body with swivel disk-joints at shoulders,
original child's cotton dress
h 36 1/2"
20-03-86
Webb Collection, 1952-60

Lady
Turin, Italy
Enrico and Elena Scavini (Lenci)
About 1930
Felt swivel head, blonde mohair wig, painted
blue eyes, painted upper and lower lashes,
two-toned red painted lips, felt body with
swivel disk-joints at shoulders and hips,
original organdy blouse, felt jumper, organdy
pinafore and hat
h 35"
20-03-85
Webb Collection, 1952-60

Turin was a large cloth-producing center in Italy especially noted for its fine woolen felts, a durable fabric used for hats and cloaks since antiquity. Elena Scavini's company used felt to make the heads and hollow molded bodies of its well-executed dolls. In 1922 the company adopted the nickname Lenci, actually an acronym for the Latin phrase "ludere est nobis constanter industria," meaning, "to play is our constant work."

The dolls were dressed in artful, highly colored outfits of felt and organdy and ranged in size from four to forty inches. According to documentation the girl in the brown dress (20-03-86) was a commercial doll used as a model for children's clothing at Arde Maison de Blanc in New York. The dolls were costly right from the start and were marketed to adults as well as to children. Advertising in the May 23, 1923, issue of *Playthings Magazine* suggested that a Lenci doll would look smart seated in the drawing room "on a hassock, to lend color in your boudoir, to decorate a corner of your limousine." By the 1930s the Lenci factory had more than 350 employees, but after suffering physical damage during World War II Signoura Scavini sold the business to the Gerrela brothers, whose descendants still run the company. Due to renewed collecting interest in 1977, the company started using old molds to make new dolls, which they manufacture today.[7]

Fig. 177
Girl
United States
About 1850
One-piece cloth head and body, black fabric hair with applied fabric cut and braided into bun in back, inked features, cloth body swing-jointed at shoulders, hips, and knees, mitten hands, original 1850s-style printed cotton stockings and felt slippers
h 15"
20-03-56
Gift of Mrs. Jerome C. Smith, 1959-185.1

Girl
New York, New York, United States
Art Fabric Mills
1899-1910
One-piece stamped cloth body, chromolithographic-printed blonde wig with printed bow, printed features, repair patches under arms, cotton pantalets and stockings, boots
h 26"
20-03-80
Gift of Miss Katharine Woodell, 1959-182.1

From the mid-1880s on, handmade dolls like the one at left eventually were superseded by mass-produced examples with the development of inexpensive chromolithographic techniques. Some printed fabric dolls were sold by the yard so that women could assemble them at home (1959.182-1), while others were sold already assembled. The textile-producing area of the Northeast was the site of many of the printing houses, including the Art Fabric Mills in New York City. The front and back of each cut-out cloth doll were printed onto cotton sheets which were then sold, ready to be cut out, sewn together, and stuffed. These dolls represented a variety of celebrity or storybook characters, or stereotypes, such as soldiers or Native Americans.

Fig. 178
French Peasant
Paris, France
Bernard Ravca
About 1950
Printed tag on fronts: Original
Ravca/Touraine/Fabrication Française
Stationary stockinet head, white mohair wig,
painted needle-sculpted features, unjointed
cloth body, original clothing and clogs
h 10 1/4"
20-03-107
Webb Collection, 1952-60

Polish Relief Fund Doll
Paris, France
About 1916
Stationary head with seam down center,
blonde fiber hair, sewn-on blue dot fabric
eyes, thread mouth, cloth body with disk-
jointed arms and legs, mitten hands, silk
scarf, cotton voile underwear, original cotton
regional dress and oilcloth boots
h 11"
20-03-113
Webb Collection, 1952-60

Lady
Probably Germany
About 1920-30
Cloth swivel head with seam down center of
face and dart from back of head to cheek,
seam down back of head, painted brown
hair, one layer unstitched applied ears, blue
bead eyes, one-stitch mouth with coloring,
felt disk-jointed arms with burlap body and
legs jointed at shoulders and hips with
metal button and wires, unmarked Steiff-
type button on blouse, original stockinet and
cotton clothing, flannel shoes
h 8 3/4"
20-03-133
Webb Collection, 1952-60

Scandinavian Newspaper Woman
Copenhagen, Denmark
Unknown date
Typed on cloth label stitched to inside edge
of skirt hem: Made by Ingeoborg Neilsen of
Copenhagen, Denmark
Painted stockinet stationary head, gray yarn
hair, molded face, painted features, unjointed cloth body, original wool skirt, denim
apron, newspaper pouch, and newspapers
h 10"
20-03-108
Webb Collection, 1952-60

Gentleman
United States
Probably Twentieth Century
Cloth stationary painted head, painted
brown hair, applied and painted papier-
mâché nose, lips, eyes, and ears, unjointed
cloth body, kid hands, original wool and velvet clothing
h 9 1/2"
20-05-06
Webb Collection, 1952-1960

The Botanist
Waltershausen, Thuringia, Germany
Kämmer & Reinhardt
About 1927
Stationary stockinet head, yarn hair, painted
needle-sculpted features, cloth body with
wire arms and legs, stockinet hands, wood-
en feet, original felt clothing, wooden stick,
and wooden pouch
h 13 1/2"
20-03-110
Webb Collection, 1952-60

Twentieth-century cloth-doll artists created characters showing the authentic costumes, customs, and personalities of real people. Examples included Ravka's French peasants representing each of the country's fifty-six provinces; regionally dressed Polish dolls sold in such resorts as Bar Harbor, Newport, and the Berkshires to raise funds to feed Polish women and children displaced by World War I; a Margarete Steiff-type caricature with blue bead eyes [8] and exaggerated features; a Scandinavian newspaper woman, and a rare example of Kämmer & Reinhardt's Botanist, with needle-sculpted features and moveable wire limbs. The last is part of the 1927 character series entitled, "My Darling Dolls," which represented many professions and trades including the Reverend, the Lawyer, the Sailor, the Salesman, the Dude, the Hobo, the Apache Dancer, the Professor, the Bell-hop, and the Bus Announcer. [9] The Botanist in the Shelburne Museum collection is the only known example of its type.

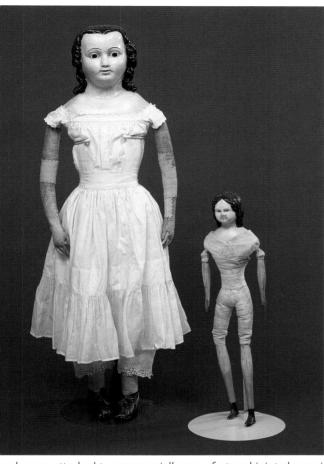

Fig. 179
Lady
United States
About 1860
Rubber shoulder head, molded painted black hair with center part hair pulled back at forehead with corkscrew curls falling from top of head onto shoulder, painted brown eyes and upper lashes, closed mouth, manufactured cloth body with leather arms swing-jointed joints at hips, shoulders, and knees, cotton pantalets, petticoat, and chemise, kid boots
h 30"
20-03-195
Webb Collection, 1952-60

Lady
United States
About 1860
Rubber shoulder head, molded painted black hair with center part waved and curled around face with long finger curls in back to shoulders, painted blue eyes and lower lashes, closed mouth, unjointed kid body with turned wooden turned lower limbs and painted boots
h 17"
20-03-22
Webb Collection, 1952-60

Nelson Goodyear patented hard rubber (#8075) in 1851, and an example was introduced at the Great Exhibition of 1851 in London.[10] This innovative material was used for doll heads licensed by the New York Rubber, India Rubber Comb, and the Metropolitan India Rubber and Vulcanite Companies. The molded hairstyles in plump ringlets copied the look of china and papier-mâché heads of the mid-to-late nineteenth century. The heads were attached to commercially manufactured jointed or unjointed cloth or kid bodies and sold through major department stores such as Montgomery Ward and F. A. O. Schwarz in New York City. The example at right, with carved wooden limbs, is based on contemporary German papier-mâché examples. Unfortunately, early rubber dolls are prone to rapid deterioration as the paint chipped and the rubber became brittle, stiff, and cracked over time. These two examples are in remarkably good condition.

Fig. 180
Girl
Reichenbach, Silesia, and Nossen, Saxony, Germany
Buschow & Beck
About 1900
Stamped on front of shoulder plate: DK Minerva Pat.
Stamped on back of shoulder plate: Germany 6
Metal shoulder head, molded blonde hair, stationary blue glass eyes, open mouth with teeth, manufactured cloth body swing-jointed at shoulders, hips, and knees with leather arms, sewed-on oilcloth boots, old cotton dress, apron, pantalets, and petticoat
19 ¹/₂"
20-03-24
Gift of Mrs. Conrad Follansbee, 1951-78.1

Joseph Schön patented metal heads in 1886-87.[11] Buschow & Beck registered the Minerva trademark in Germany for sheet metal heads and both dressed and undressed dolls attached to cloth bodies. These dolls were distributed by Alfred Vischer & Co. and Borgfeldt in New York City, as well as by Sears, Roebuck & Co. about 1900. The metal was usually tin-coated iron, and, although the dolls were clearly unbreakable, the paintwork quickly discolored and was easily chipped. Metal-headed dolls were also cold to the touch and never achieved the popularity of their bisque or composition relatives.

Notes

Introduction

1. Electra Havemeyer Webb, "The Shelburne Museum and How it Grew" (Lecture, Colonial Williamsburg Antiques Forum, Williamsburg VA, January 30, 1958), 1:20, Electra Havemeyer Webb Papers, Shelburne Museum Archives.
2. Electra Havemeyer Webb, confidential memorandum, to Kenneth Chorley, January 28, 1948, 8:9, Electra Havemeyer Webb Papers, Shelburne Museum Archives.
3. Karin Calvert, *Children in the House* (Boston: Northeastern University Press, 1992), 6.
4. Calvert, *Children in the House,* 127.
5. Mary Lynn Stevens Heininger et al., *A Century of Childhood,* 1820-1920 (Rochester, NY: Margaret Woodbury Strong Museum), 28.

Technical Tidbits

1. Shelburne Museum conservators keep a glass panel with known samples of various materials on it. While the appearance under ultraviolet light is not be enough to identify a particular coating material as hide glue, dammar varnish, or linseed oil, conservators compare the behavior of a material on an artifact under ultraviolet light to the known materials to characterize the unknowns.
2. Betsy Geiser, "Barbie's Great-Great Grandmother: A Study of the Manufacture and Materials of Queen Anne Style Dolls." In *Student Papers from the 26th Conference of the Association of North American Graduate Programs in Conservation, 27-29 April 2000* (Washington, DC: Smithsonian Center for Materials Research and Education, 2002), 10-23.
3. Melting-point measurements were made by Anapaum Garg in the Chemistry Department at the University of Vermont.
4. John S. Mills and Raymond White, *The Organic Chemistry of Museum Objects* (London: Butterworths, 1987), 42, 45
5. Radiographs were taken at Fletcher Allen Hospital, Burlington, VT; Vermont Radiology, South Burlington, VT; and Porter Hospital, Middlebury, VT.
6. Caroline Goodfellow to the author, February 21, 2001.
7. Geiser, "Barbie's Great-Great Grandmother."
8. Robert L. Feller, "Barium Sulfate—Natural and Synthetic."In *Artists' Pigments: A Handbook of their History and Characteristics,* volume 1 ed. Robert L. Feller (Washington, DC: National Gallery of Art, 1986), 47.
9. Patent text and drawings are available at the U.S. Patent Office's Web site, http://www.uspto.gov.

Wooden Dolls

1. Donna A. Kaonis, "The Heart of the Tree," *Doll News,* Summer 2002, 23-27.
2. *Daily Courant* (London), February 8, 1718.
3. Wendy Lavitt, *Dolls: The Knopf Collectors' Guides to American Antiques* (New York: Alfred A. Knopf, 1983), 312.
4. James Laver, "Examining Early English Woodens," *Costume,* quoted in *Dolls,* June/July 1992, 77.

Papier Mâché

1. Peter Owen, *Fashions in Hair: The First Five Thousand Years* (Edinburgh: R & R Clark, 1965), 468.
2. Christiane Gräfnitz, *German Papier-Mâché Dolls,* 1760-1860 (Duisburg, Germany: Verlag Puppen & Spielzeug, 1994), 20.
3. Grafnitz, *German Papier-Mâché Dolls,* 28-33, and Mary Gorham Krombholz, *The Story of German Doll Making, 1530-2000* (Grantsville, MD: Hobby House Press, 2001), 16-18.
4. Owen, *Fashions in Hair,* 473.

. Gräfnitz, *German Papier-Mâché Dolls,* 43.
. Christiane Gräfnitz, e-mail to author, September 24, 2003.
. Gräfnitz, *German Papier-Mâché Dolls,* 43.
. Ibid., 47.
. Dorothy S. Coleman, Elizabeth Ann Coleman, and Evelyn Jane Coleman, *The Collector's Encyclopedia of Dolls*
New York: Crown Publishers, 1968), 1: 200.

Wax Dolls

. Pauline Flick, "The Magic of Wax," *Dolls,* Spring 1984, 46; Lynne Murray, "The Allure of Wax," *Antique Doll
Collector,* May 2003, 37.
. Murray, "The Allure of Wax," 39.
. Jürgen Cieslik and Marianne Cieslik. *German Doll Encyclopedia* (Cumberland, MD: Hobby House Press, 1985),
11, 330.
. Cieslik, *German Doll Encyclopedia,* 311,330.
. Eleanor St. George, *The Dolls of Yesterday,* (New York, Bonanza Books, 1948), 92.
. Gräfnitz, *German Papier-Mâché Dolls,* 43.
. Cieslik, *German Doll Encyclopedia,* 50, and Coleman, Coleman, and Coleman, *Collector's Encyclopedia of Dolls,* 1: 270.
. Constance King, *Collectors' History of Dolls* (New York, St. Martin's Press, 1978), 248-49.

China Dolls

. Mary Gorham Krombholz, *Identifying German Chinas, 1840s-1930s* (Grantsville, MD: Hobby House Press, 2004), 9.
. Krombholz, *Identifying German Chinas,* 17.
. Ibid., 115.
. See Ibid.
. Ibid., 71.
. Ibid., 31,41.
. Quoted in C. Willet and Phillis Cunningham, *The History of Underclothes* (Mineola, NY: Dover Publications,
992), 148.
. Julie Barrow, e-mail attachment to author, December 4, 2003, entitled Worcester History Museum, Worcester,
Massachusetts, Royal Worcester Corsets, 1890 Catalog, 11.
. Jo Elizabeth Gerkin, *Wonderful Dolls of Papier-Mâché* (Lincoln, NE: Union College Press, 1970), 117-18.
0. Christiane Gräfnitz, "The Doll Heads of KPM," *Doll News,* Winter 2004, 8-16.
1. Krombholz, *Identifying German Chinas,* 75.
2. Ibid., 75-92.
3. See Ibid., 78, for identical model.
4. See Krombholz, *Identifying German Chinas,* 72-73, for identical example.
5. Mary McClellan, *The History of American Costume* (New York: Tudor Publishing Co, 1904), quoted in Ibid., 52.
6. Krombholz, *Identifying German Chinas,* 52.
7. Mary Gorham Krombholz, "A.W. Fr. Kister Porcelain Factory," *Doll News,* June 2002, 32.
8. Norah Waugh, *Corsets and Crinolines.* (London: B. T. Batsford, 1954), 79. See also Willet and Cunningham,
History of Underclothes, 163.
9. See Krombholz, *Identifying German Chinas,* 154, for identical model
0. Ibid., 152.
1. Ibid., 105, 108.
2. Ibid., 103.
3. Ibid., 38.
4. Ibid., 101.
5. Ibid., 96.

26. Ibid., 96-7.

27. See Ibid., 95, for curly-top model reproduced from *Godey's Lady's Magazine,* August 1867.

28. Ibid., 85-6.

Bisque Dolls

1. Maree Tarnowska, *Fashion Dolls* (Cumberland, MD: Hobby House Press, 1986), 13.

2. Coleman, Coleman, and Coleman, *Collector's Encyclopedia of Dolls,* 1: 418.

3. Ibid., 219.

4. Theriault, "Lady Dolls of the 19th Century," *Antique Doll Collector,* 5, 11, December 2003, 50.

5. Coleman, Coleman, and Coleman, *Collector's Encyclopedia of Dolls,* 240.

6. Ibid., 332.

7. Ibid., 239.

8. Tarnowska, *Fashion dolls,* 6.

9. "Lettre d'un Bebe Jumeau à sa Petite Mère," reprinted in *Spinning Wheel,* January-February 1965, 16-17.

10. Coleman, Coleman, and Coleman, *Collector's Encyclopedia of Dolls,* 511.

11. Ibid., 94.

12. Cieslik and Cieslik, *Encyclopedia,* 147.

13. Mary Gorham Krombholz, *German Porcelain Dolls, 1836-200* (Grantsville, MD: Hobby House Press, 2002), 64, and Cieslik and Cieslik, *Encyclopedia,* 158.

Parian Dolls

1. Many thanks to Mary Krombholz for her telephone and e-mail consultation based on her ongoing research of German parian-type dolls.

2. Mary Krombholz, e-mail to author, December 9, 2003.

3. Krombholz, *Identifying German Chinas,* 115.

4. Ibid., 115.

5. Ibid., 98-100.

6. Ibid.,61.

7. Ibid., 71.

8. Coleman, Coleman, and Coleman, *Collector's Encyclopedia of Dolls,* 1: 190.

9. Krombholz, *German Porcelain Dolls,* 9.

10. Ibid., 73.

11. Ibid., 67-68.

12. Cieslik and Cieslik, *Encyclopedia,* 180.

13. Mary Krombholz, e-mail to author, December 26, 2003.

14. Women's History Resource Web site, King's College History Department, University of Cambridge, Cambridge, England.

15. Jo Elizabeth Gerkin, *Wonderful Dolls of Papier Mâché* (Lincoln, NE: Union College Press, 1970), 48.

16. Dorothy S. Coleman, "Philip Goldsmith (1844-1894), An American Dollmaker," *Spinning Wheel,* October 1970, 12-14.

17. Krombholz, *German Porcelain Dolls,* 100.

Cloth Dolls

1. Jan Foulke, "Izannah Walker Dolls," *Doll Reader,* February/March 1982, 33.

2. Coleman, Coleman, and Coleman, *Collector's Encyclopedia of Dolls,* 2: 272, fig, 583

3. Ibid., 2: figs. 605a and b.

4. Linda Edward, *Cloth Dolls from Ancient to Modern* (Atglen, PA: Schiffer Publishing, 1997), 34.

5. Lavitt, 239.

. Dorothy McGonagle, *A Celebration of American Dolls from the Collections of the Strong Museum*, 99..

. Edward, *Cloth Dolls*, 86.

. Caroline Goodfellow, *The Ultimate Doll Book* (New York: Dorling Kindersley, 1993), 97.

. Eugenia Shorrock, "The Men in My Life," *Doll Collectors Manual* 1983 (np: The Doll Collectors of America, 1983), 112.

o. Florence Theriault, *Dolls: The Early Years, 1780-1880* (Annapolis, MD: Theriault's, 1989), chap. 3 .

1. Coleman, Coleman, and Coleman, *Collector's Encyclopedia of Dolls*, 1: 446.

Appendix A

orcelain Factories and Doll Factories Represented at the Shelburne Museum

he majority of doll-related porcelain products were made for one hundred years from 1840 to about 1940.

or most firms, only the founding dates are listed because in most cases it is not known with any certainty when oll production specifically started and stopped.

Bisque

Name of Firm	Business Location	Date(s)
rmand Marseille	Köppelsdorf, Thuringia, Germany	1884
ru Jne. & Cie	Paris and Montreuil-sous-Bois, France	1866-99
ebrüder Heubach	Lichte and Sonneberg, Thuringia, Germany	1804
meau	Paris and Montreuil-sous-Bois, France	1842-99
abery and Delphieu	Paris, France	1856-98
lies Steiner	Paris, France	1855-91
imon & Halbig	Gräfenhain, Thuringia, Germany	1869

he Simon & Halbig porcelain factory made the entire group of 100 series character dolls for the Kämmer & einhardt doll factory (founded 1885) in Waltershausen, Thuringia, Germany

China and Parian

Name of Firm	Business Location	Date(s)
lt, Beck & Gottschalck	Nauendorf, Thuringia, Germany	1854
onta & Böhme	Pössneck, Thuringia, Germany	1790
ornheim, Koch & Fischer	Gräfenroda, Thuringia, Germany	1856
ertwig & Co.	Katzhütte, Thuringia, Germany	1864
estner & Co.	Ohrdruf, Thuringia, Germany	1816-1938
.W. Fr. Kister	Scheibe-Alsbach, Thuringia, Germany	1837
.F. Kling & Co.	Ohrdurf, Thuringia, Germany	1834
loster Veilsdorf	Veilsdorf, Thuringia, Germany	1765
PM	Meissen and Berlin, Germany	1710 and 1763
Königliche Porzellan Manufactur, King's Porcelain Factory)		
oyal Copenhagen	Denmark	1844

Cloth

Name of Firm	Business Location	Date(s)
Martha Jenks Chase	Pawtucket, Rhode Island, United States	About 1880s-1925
Käthe Kruse	Bad Kösen, Germany	About 1904-1930
Liberty & Co.	London, England	1873-present
Lenci	Turin, Italy	1920
(Enrico and Elena Scavini)		
Bernard Ravca	Paris, France	About 1924
Izannah Walker	Central Falls, Rhode Island, United States	About 1855-1886

Papier Mâché

Name of Firm	Business Location	Date(s)
Cuno and Otto Dressel	Sonneberg, Germany	1700
Ludwig Greiner	Philadelphia, Pennsylvania, United States	1840
Philip Lerch	Philadelphia, Pennsylvania, United States	1858
Müller & Strassburger	Sonneberg, Germany	1844
Andreas Voit	Hildburghausen, Thuringia, Germany	1816

Wood

Name of Firm	Business Location	Date(s)
Albert Schoenhut & Co.	Philadelphia, Pennsylvania, United States	1872
Cooperative Manufacturing Co.	Springfield, Vermont, United States	1873-74
Door of Hope Mission	Shanghai, China	1902
Jointed Doll Co.	Springfield, Vermont, United States	1874-1885

Wax

Name of Firm	Business Location	Date(s)
Fritz Bartenstein	Sonneberg, Germany	1864-1905
Anthony Bazzoni	London, England	1843-78
John Edwards	London, England	1856-84
Louis Lindner & Söhne	Sonneberg, Germany	1847
Mme. Augusta Montanari	London, England	1851
Mrs. Lucy Peck	London, England	1891-1921

Appendix B

Glossary

Articulation – the attachment of doll limbs by various methods that permit movement.

Ball joint – an articulated joint usually formed by a wooden ball between two sockets that are connected by an elastic or a metal spring to allow movement in several directions.

Batiste – a soft, sheer cotton linen fabric of plain weave used for lingerie, dresses and blouses.

Bébé – a doll that has the proportions of a young child about the age of six to twelve with a shorter, fatter body than a lady doll.

Bisque – short for the term "biscuit," referring to unglazed porcelain. Doll heads made of bisque are usually tinted and fired twice. They have a matte surface finish.

China – glazed porcelain. Like bisque, these doll heads are painted and fired at least twice twice and also glazed.

They have a shiny surface.

Dolly-face - a term describing a girl doll with a standardized sweet, smiling expression.

Flange joint - an articulated joint in which the bottom of the neck and the top of the shoulder fit together with a flat surface. Sometimes there is a flange or rim around the edge of the joint.

Flirty eyes - eyes that move from side to side depending on the position of the weight inside the head.

Flocked hair - hair simulated by gluing thin fuzzy fibers or wool or felt to a boy or baby doll's head.

Guimpe - a short blouse often with sleeves, usually worn with a pinafore type of dress; a chemisette or yoke with high-standing collar made of sheer lace or fine net to fill in the neckline when low-necked dresses were introduced.

Gusset - a triangular, tapered piece of fabric inserted in garment for additional strength or to adjust the fit. After the mid-nineteenth century used often for joints on French leather doll bodies.

Intaglio - carved and painted eyes with the iris and pupil concave.

Mohair - the hair from an angora goat used to make a doll's wig.

Mortise-and-tenon joint - a method of joint articulation in which a projecting section (tenon or tongue) at the end of one limb is fitted into the corresponding carved-out section (mortise or groove) at the end of the other limb and secured with a peg or pin. This permits the forward and backward movement of the limb.

Needle-sculpture - a technique in which needle and thread are used to give a third dimension to fabric. Often used to form the facial features of a cloth doll.

Open/closed mouth - a molded doll's mouth with parted lips, sometimes showing teeth or tongue, but with no actual opening cut into the head.

Painted features - a term used to designate a doll's eyes, eyebrows, and mouth.

Paperweight eyes - blown-glass eyes with the depth of color and quality of paperweights.

Papier Mâché - the mixture of wet paper pulp that has been heated with various fillers (flour, sand, clay, chalk) and binders (animal glue, gum arabic). The resulting dough is pressed into plaster of paris molds to form doll heads.

Paraffin - a waxy substance that is white, odorless, and translucent; used for making some doll heads.

Parian - an unglazed fine, white, untinted bisque.

Pate - the crown of the head concealed beneath a wig; often a piece of cork or plaster used to cover the hole made in the crown of some dolls' heads to which the wigs were attached.

Peg wooden - a doll made entirely of wood with mortise-and-tenon joints that are pegged.

Proper right or left- a term that refers to either the right of left side of the doll from anatomical position, rather than from the viewer's perspective.

Ruching - a strip of silk, crepe, chiffon, or lace pleated or gathered; used as dress trimming usually at neck or wrist.

Shoulder head - the head and shoulder of a doll made as a single unit and of different material from that of the body.

Shoulder plate - the shoulder part of a shoulder head with a joint at the neck.

Sleep eyes - eyes that open and close by various methods and devices such as internal weights, external wires, pull strings, etc.

Socket head - a doll head with a neck joint that enables the head to swivel in all directions. The hemispherical bottom of the neck fits into a corresponding socket in the top of the shoulder plate.

Spoon hand - a hand made of wood or ceramic carved or molded in a cupped shape lacking separated fingers but often having a separate thumb.

Spermaceti - a wax found in the head cavities and blubber of the sperm whale; used to make doll heads.

Stockinet - a flat or tubular knitted fabric originally used for stockings.

Stomacher - a decorative article of dress worn over the breast and reaching to the waist or below with the gown laced over it.

Swivel head - a doll head that turns in a socket.

Tarlatan - a thin, open-mesh, transparent muslin slightly stiffened; used for stiffening in garments, fancy-dress costumes, Christmas stockings.

Threaded - a term used to describe blown-glass eyes with small threads of glass drawn through the material.

Tuck comb - a type of peg-wooden doll with an integrally carved and painted wooden comb standing on top of the head.

Wax-over-papier-mâché - a doll head or limb that has been dipped in wax.

Wax - a doll head or limb created of solid or hollow wax made from spermaceti, paraffin, or beeswax.

Selected Bibliography

Borger, Mona. *Chinas, Dolls for Study and Admiration*. San Francisco: Borger Publications, 1983.

Bradfield, Nancy. *Costume in Detail, 1730-1930*. London: George G. Harrap, 1968.

Cieslik, Jürgen, and Marianne Cieslik. *German Doll Studies*. Annapolis, MD: Theriault's Gold Horse Publishing, 1999.

—. *German Doll Encyclopedia*. Cumberland, MD: Hobby House Press, 1985.

—. *German Doll Marks & Identification Book*. Cumberland, MD: Hobby House Press, 1986.

Coleman, Dorothy S., Elizabeth Ann Coleman, and Evelyn Jane Coleman. *The Collector's Encyclopedia of Dolls*. 2 vols. New York: Crown Publishers, 1968, 1986.

Edward, Linda. *Cloth Dolls from Ancient to Modern*. Atglen, PA: Schiffer Publishing, 1997.

Foulke, Jan. *Insider's Guide to China Doll Collecting*. Grantsville, MD: Hobby House Press, 1995.

Foulke, Jan. *Insider's Gude to German 'Dolly' Collecting*. Grantsville, MD: Hobby House Press, 1995.

Gerkin, Jo Elizabeth. *Wonderful Dolls of Papier Mâché*. Lincoln, NE: Union College Press, 1970.

Gerkin, Jo Elizabeth. *Wonderful Dolls of Wax*. Wichita, KS: Calico Print Shop, 1964.

Goodfellow, Caroline. *The Ultimate Doll Book*. New York: Dorling Kindersley, 1993.

—. *Understanding Dolls*. Woodbridge, Suffolk, England: Antique Collectors' Club, 1983.

Gräfnitz, Christiane. *German Papier-Mâché Dolls, 1760-1860*. Duisburg, Germany: Verlag Puppen & Spielzeug, 1994.

—. "The Doll Heads of KPM." *Doll News*, Winter 2004, 8-16.

Grout, Jean. "A China Doll Primer." *Antique Doll Collector* 3, 4, May/June 2000, 23-30.

Krombholz, Mary Gorham. *German Porcelain Dolls, 1836-2002*. Grantsville, MD: Hobby House Press, 2002.

—. *Identifying German Chinas, 1840s-1930s*. Grantsville, MD: Hobby House Press, 2004.

—. *The Story of German Doll Making, 1530-2000*. Grantsville, MD: Hobby House Press, 2001.

Lavitt, Wendy. *Doll: The Knopf Collectors' Guides to American Antiques*. New York: Alfred A. Knopf, 1983.

McGonagle, Dorothy A. *A Celebration of American Dolls from the Collections of the Strong Museum*. Grantsville, MD: Hobby House Press, 1997.

Noble, John Darcy. *Selected Writings of John Darcy Noble: Favorite Articles from Dolls Magazine, 1982-1995*. Cumberland, MD: Portfolio Press, 1999.

Owen, Peter. *Fashions in Hair: The First Five Thousand Years*. Edinburgh: R & R Clark, 1965.

Picken, Mary Brooks. *The Fashion Dictionary*. New York: Funk & Wagnall's, 1957.

Seeley, Mildred. *Beloved China Dolls*. Livonia, MI: Scott Publications, 1996.

Smith, Patricia R. *China and Parian Dolls*. Paducah, KY: Collector Books, n.d.

Tarnowska, Maree. *Fashion Dolls*. Cumberland, MD: Hobby House Press, 1986.

Theriault Florence. *Dolls: The Early Years, 1780-1880*. Annapolis, MD: Theriault's, 1989.

—. *More Dolls: The Early Years, 1780-1910*. Annapolis, MD: Gold Horse Publishing, 1992.

"UFDC List of Accepted Terms," United Federation of Doll Clubs, Inc. (N.p., 1995).

Waugh, Norah. *Corsets and Crinolines*. London: B. T. Batsford, 1954.

Webb, Electra Havemeyer. Electra Havemeyer Webb Papers, Shelburne Museum Archives, Shelburne, Vermont (abbreviated EHW Papers).

Willet, C., and Phillis Cunningham. *The History of Underclothes*. Mineola, NY: Dover Publications, 1992.